ORIGO

STEPPING STONES 2.0

COMPREHENSIVE MATHEMATICS

W9-CPC-169

AUTHORS

James Burnett
Rosemary Irons
Peter Stowasser
Allan Turton

PROGRAM CONSULTANTS

Diana Lambdin
Frank Lester, Jr.
Kit Norris

CONTRIBUTING WRITER

Beth Lewis

PRACTICE BOOK

ORIGO EDUCATION

INTRODUCTION

ORIGO STEPPING STONES 2.0

The *ORIGO Stepping Stones 2.0* program has been developed to provide a balanced approach to teach and learn mathematics. It has been developed by a team of experts to create a world-class comprehensive math program. Each kindergarten student has two books.

THIS PRACTICE BOOK

Regular and meaningful practice is a hallmark of *ORIGO Stepping Stones 2.0*. Each module in the Practice Book includes pages that revisit content from the previous Student Journal module to maintain concepts and skills, and pages that practice numeral writing or computation to promote fluency. Each module also includes a one-page review of two big ideas from the Student Journal. For example, Review 1 revisits two big ideas from Module 1 in the Student Journal.

PERFORATED PAGES

The perforation in this book allows students to remove and cut out images for use in activities.

Space for the student's name when a page is removed.

Module and lesson

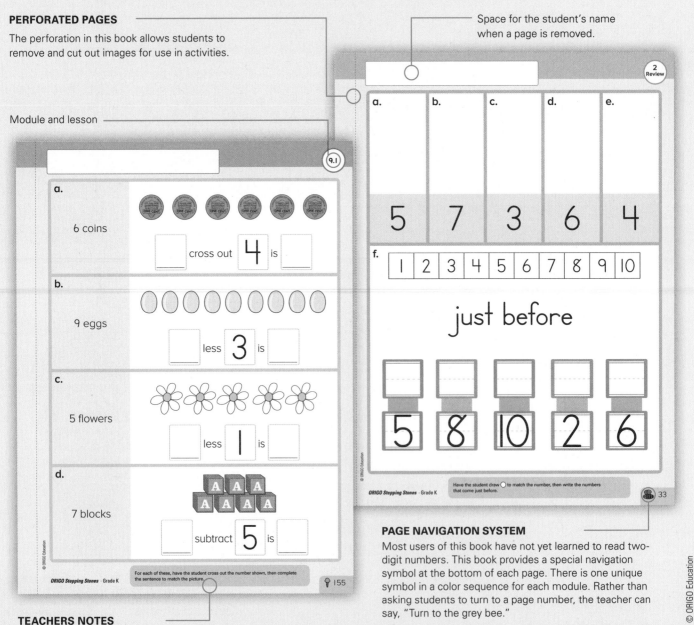

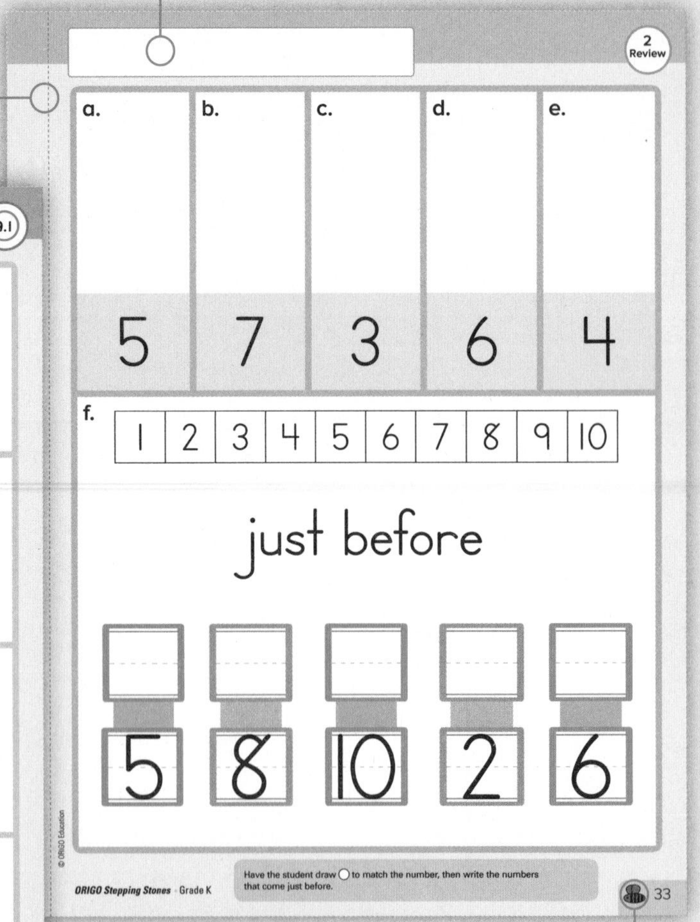

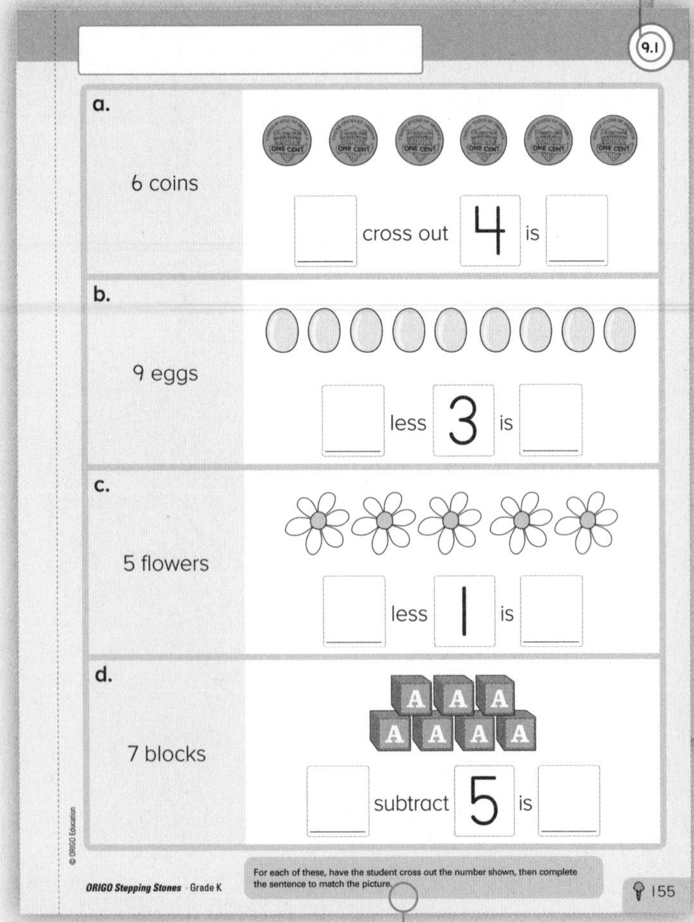

PAGE NAVIGATION SYSTEM

Most users of this book have not yet learned to read two-digit numbers. This book provides a special navigation symbol at the bottom of each page. There is one unique symbol in a color sequence for each module. Rather than asking students to turn to a page number, the teacher can say, "Turn to the grey bee."

TEACHERS NOTES

Brief notes reduce instructions for students to read.

© ORIGO Education

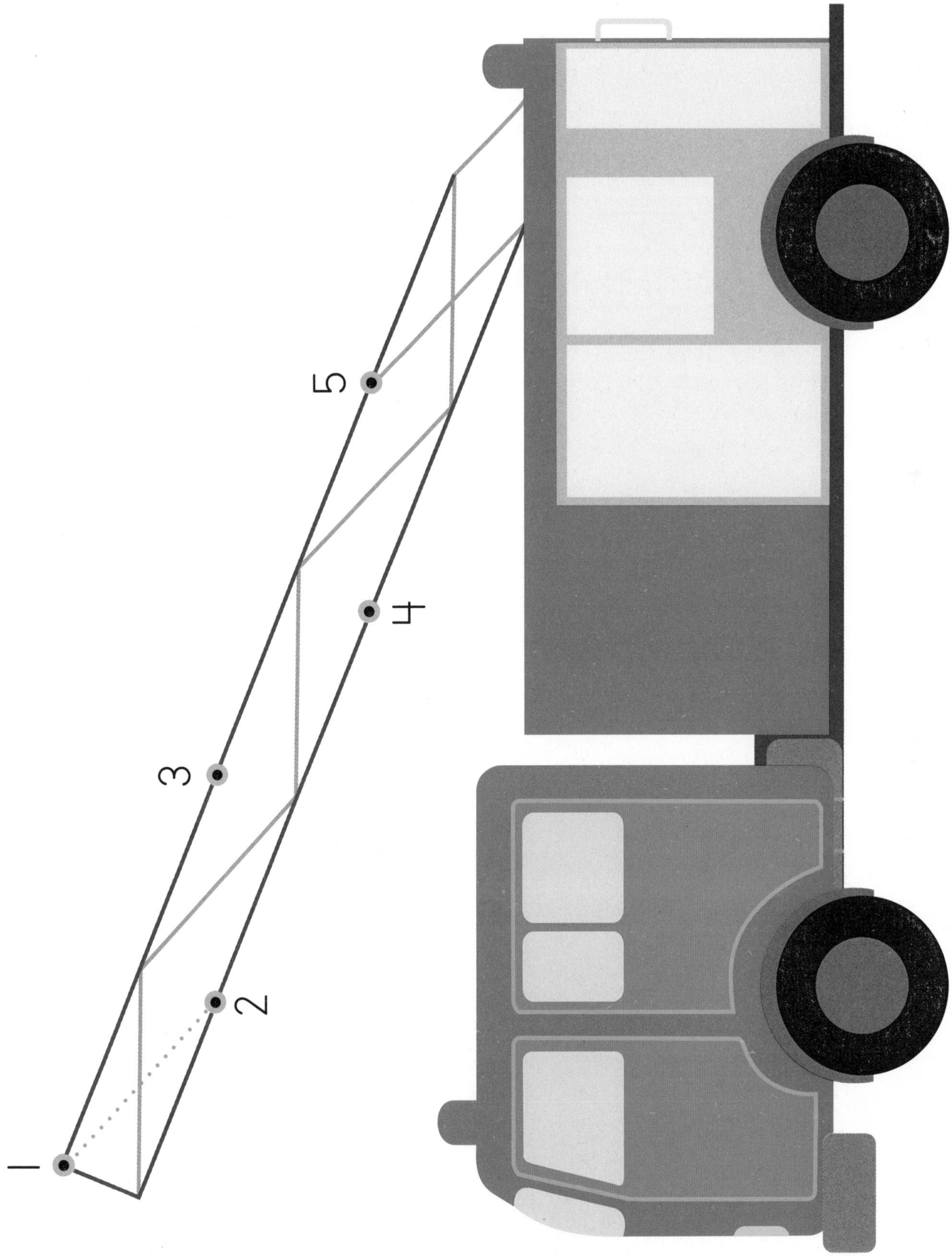

© ORIGO Education

Have the student draw lines from 1 to 5 while saying the numbers aloud.

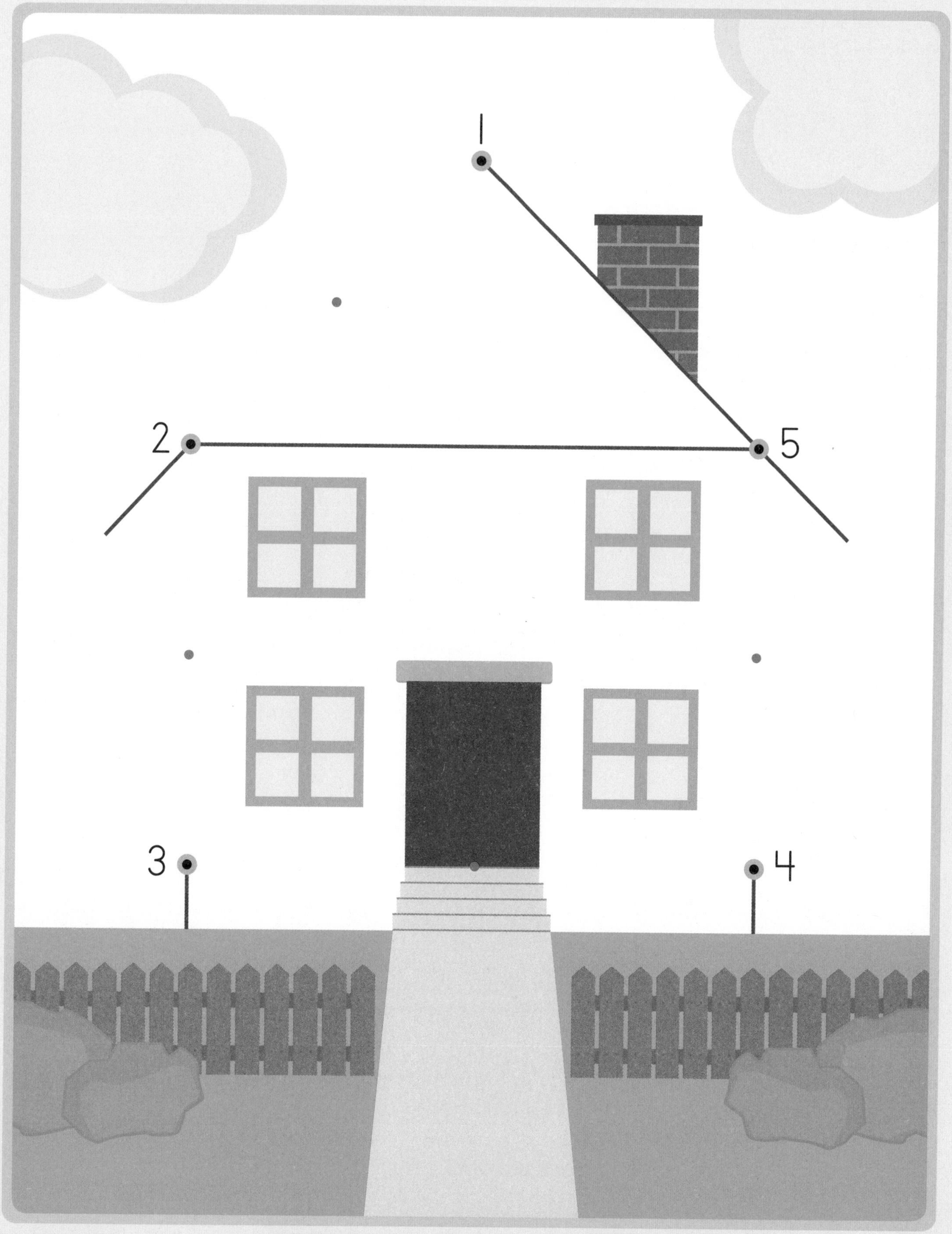

© ORIGO Education

Have the student draw lines from 1 to 5 while saying the numbers aloud.
They can pause on the halfway points if necessary.

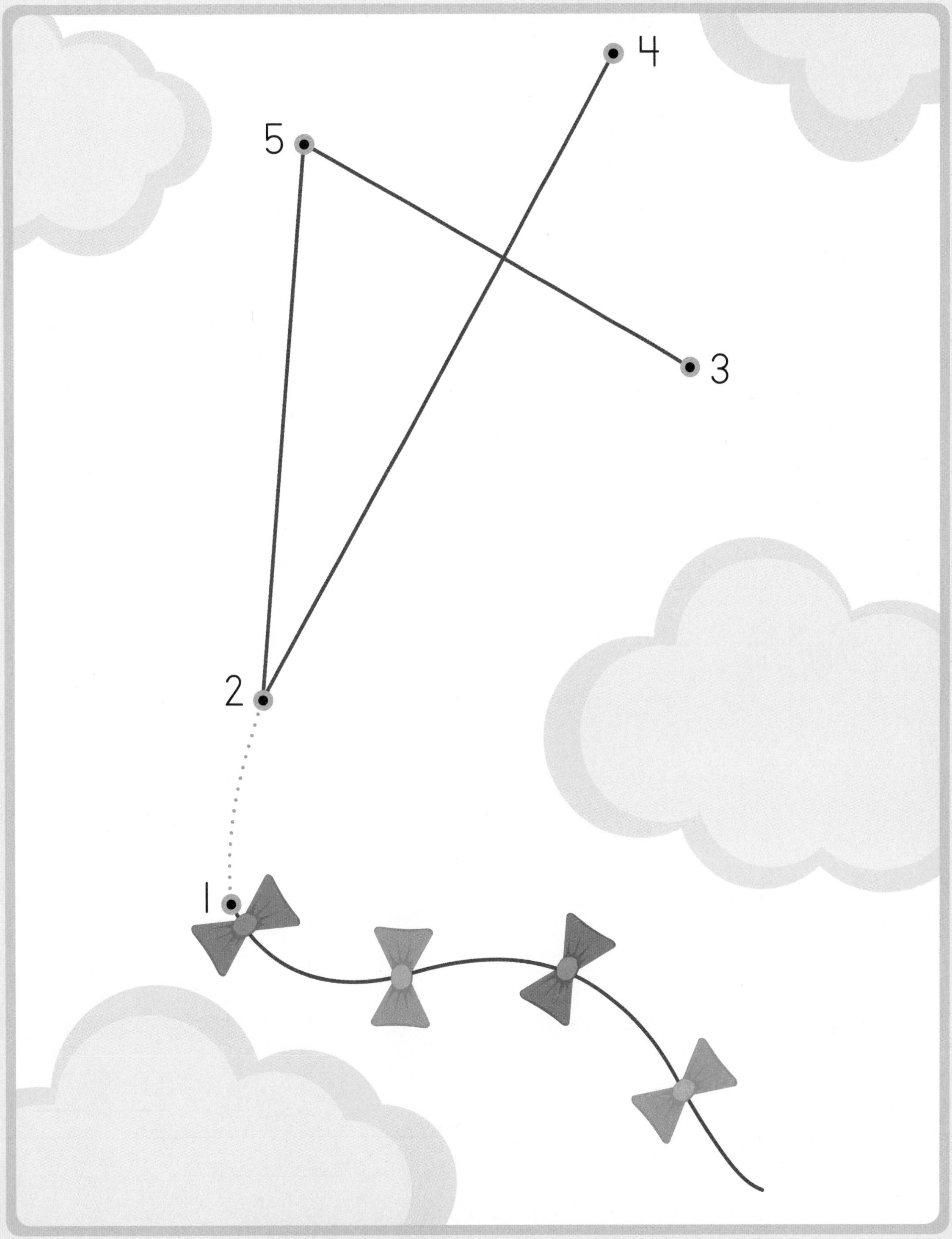

© ORIGO Education

Have the student draw lines from 1 to 5 while saying the numbers aloud.

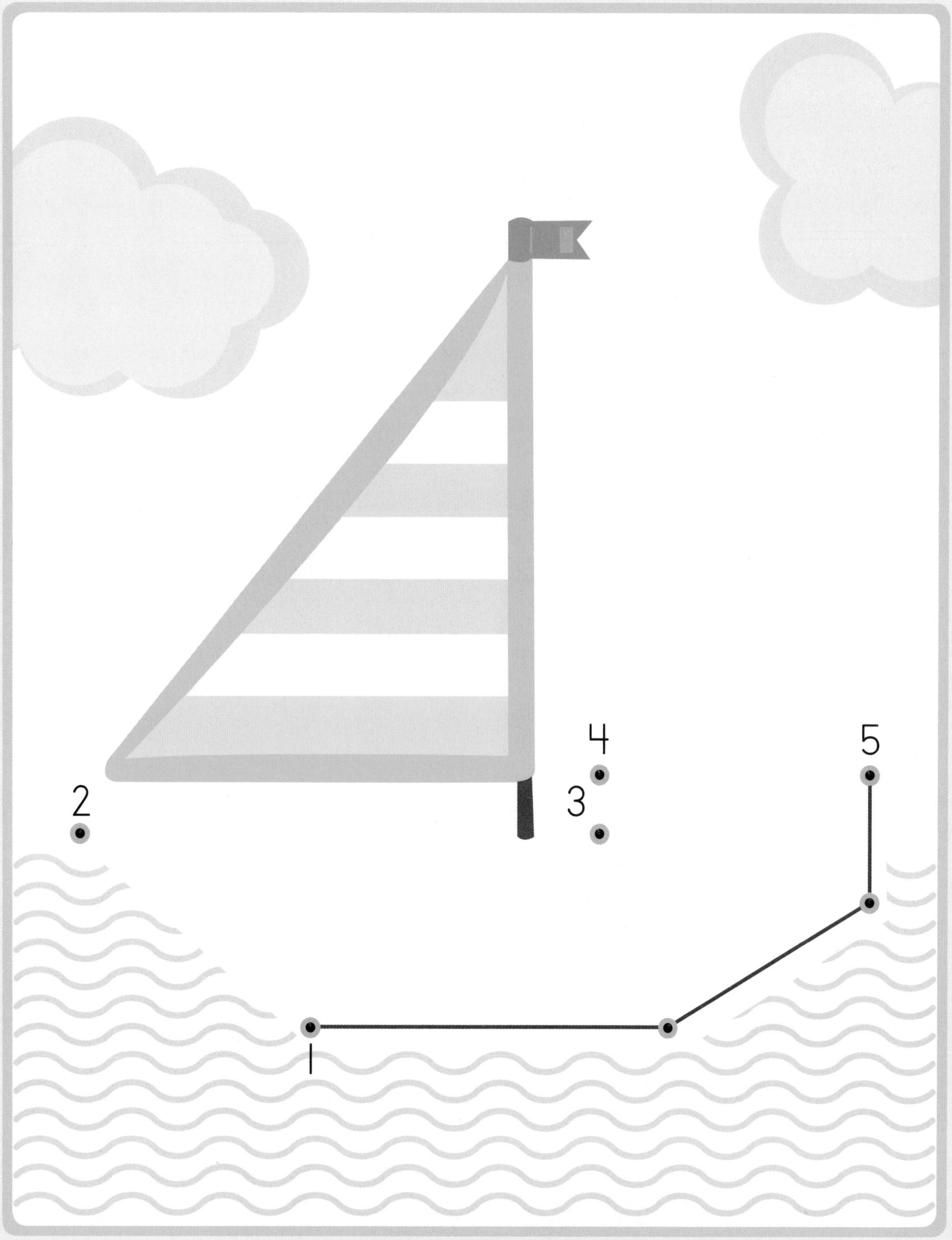

© ORIGO Education

Have the student draw lines from 1 to 5 while saying the numbers aloud.

Have the student draw lines from 1 to 5 while saying the numbers aloud.
They can pause at the red halfway points if necessary.

© ORIGO Education

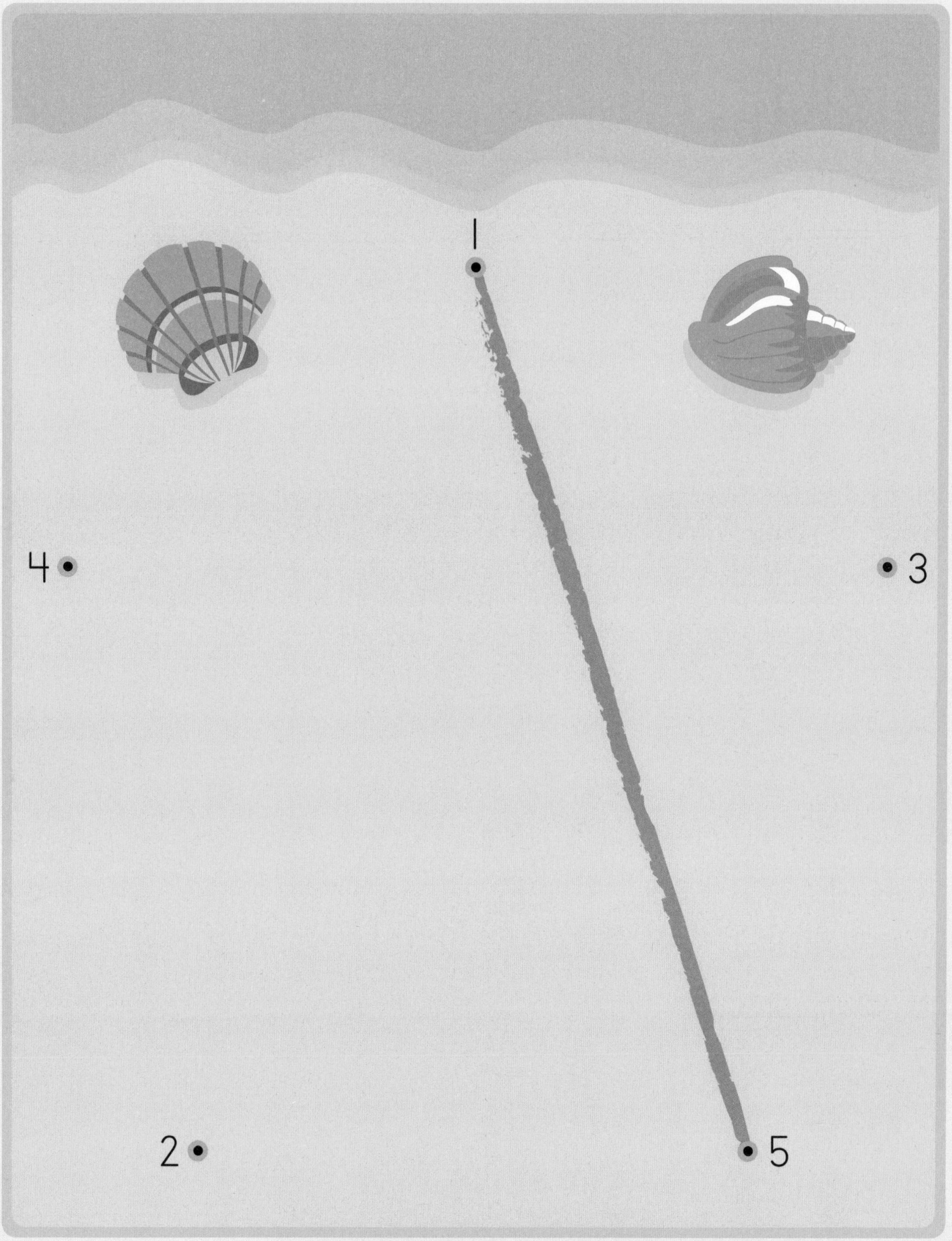

© ORIGO Education

Have the student draw lines from 1 to 5 while saying the numbers aloud.

a.

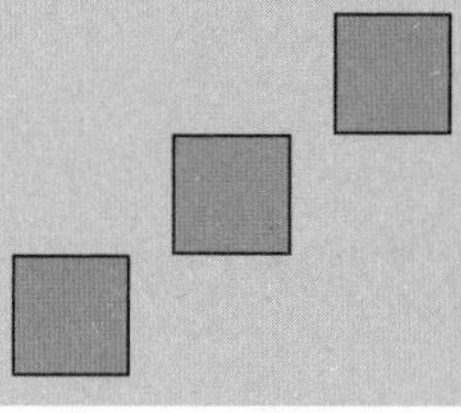

b.

c.

d. 2

e. 5

f. 3

© ORIGO Education

Have the student place and trace around counters to match each quantity or numeral.

© ORIGO Education

Have the student cut out the pictures, then paste them into groups on a sheet of paper. Ask the student to describe the groups they made.

a.

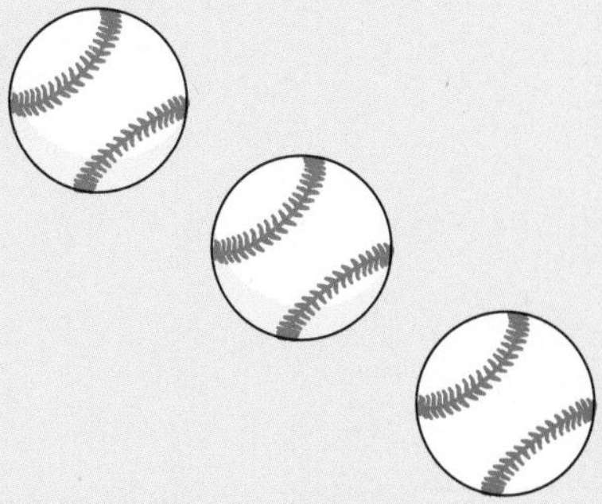

b.

c.

d.

e.

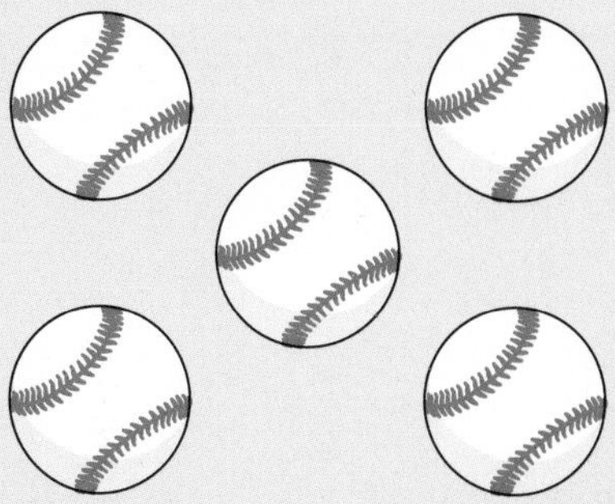

© ORIGO Education

Have the student place and trace around counters to match the quantity of baseballs shown. Ask the student to count each group aloud.

© ORIGO Education

Have the student draw lines from 1 to 6 while saying the numbers aloud.

a. 2

b. 5

c. 1

d. 4

e. 3

© ORIGO Education

Have the student place and trace around counters to match the numeral. Ask the student to draw a face (☺) on each and count aloud the number in each group.

a. 3

b. 5

c. 1

d. 4

e. 2

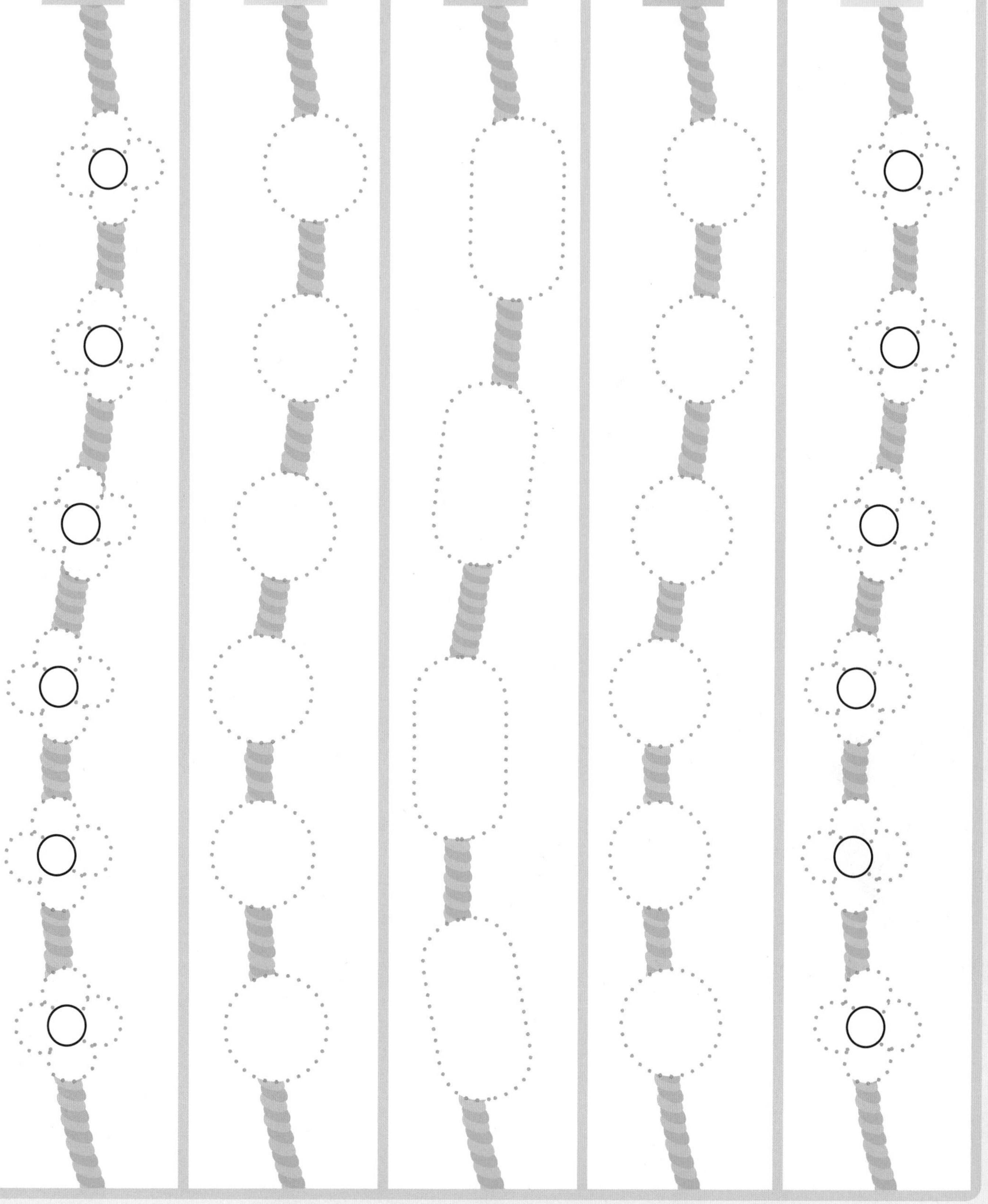

Have the student trace and color beads to match the numeral.
Ask the student to read, count, and say the number of beads on each thread.

© ORIGO Education

a.

b.

c.

© ORIGO Education

ORIGO Stepping Stones • Grade K

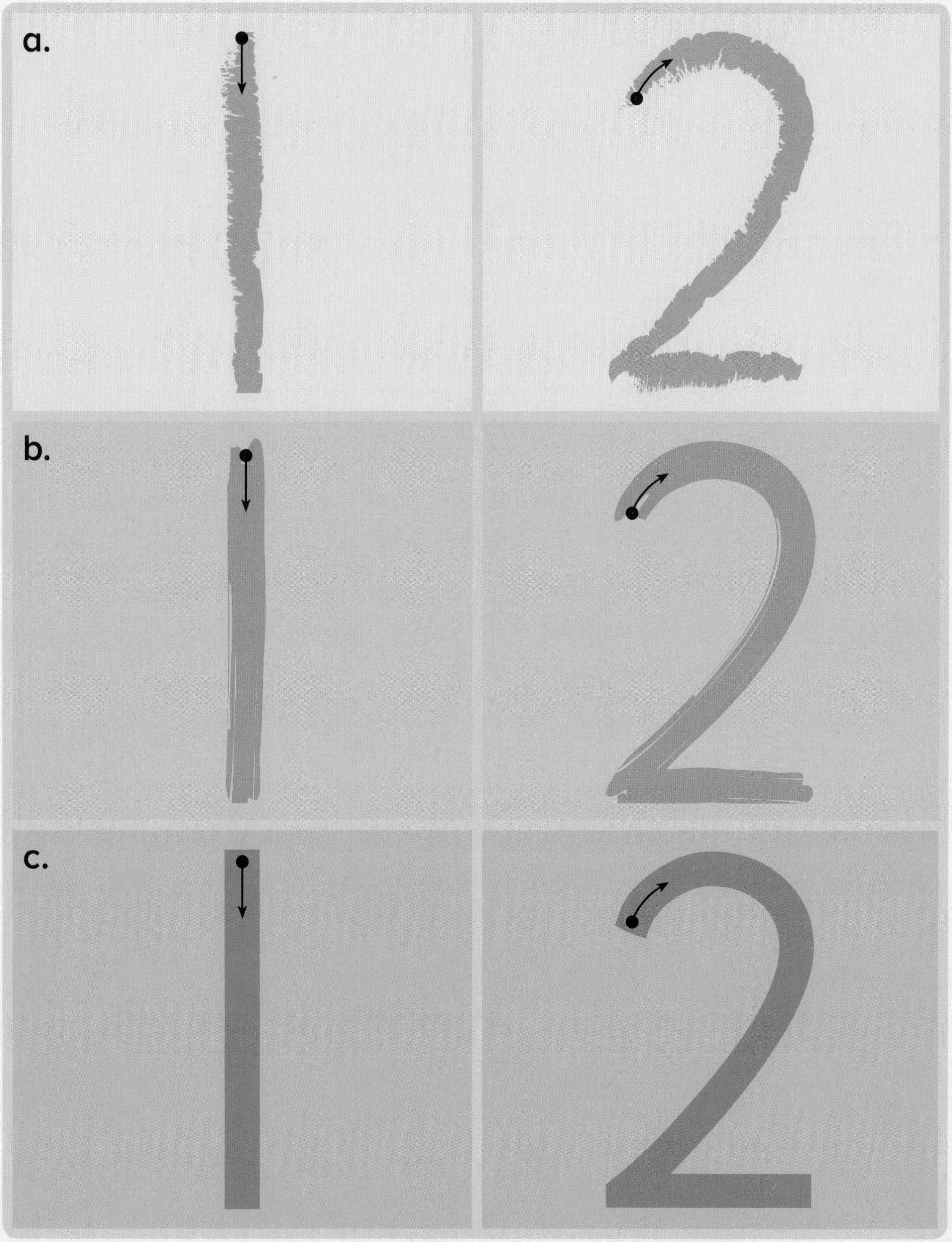

Have the student say each number aloud, then trace over the numeral with their finger and write it three times.

© ORIGO Education

Read the labels aloud. Have the student cut out and sort the pictures into two groups, then describe their sort. Ask the student to sort in another way. Have the student paste one of their sorts onto a sheet of paper.

Are dogs your favorite pet?	
yes	no

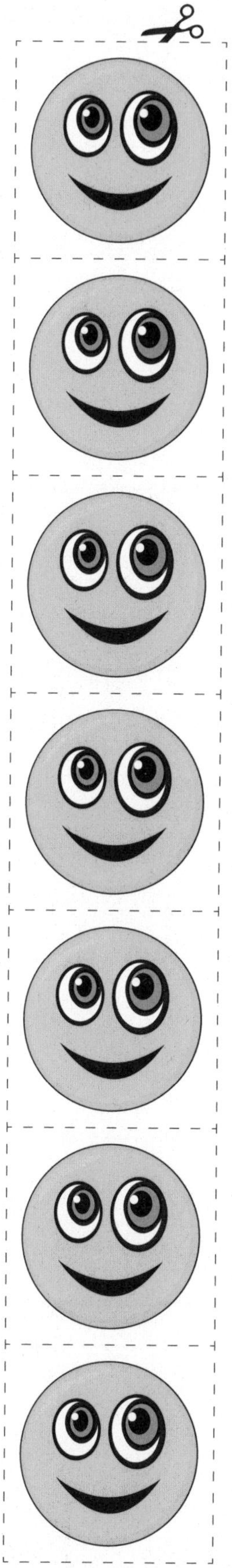

© ORIGO Education

Have the student cut out the face pictures and ask seven people the question "Are dogs your favorite pet?" Then paste the faces in the appropriate columns.

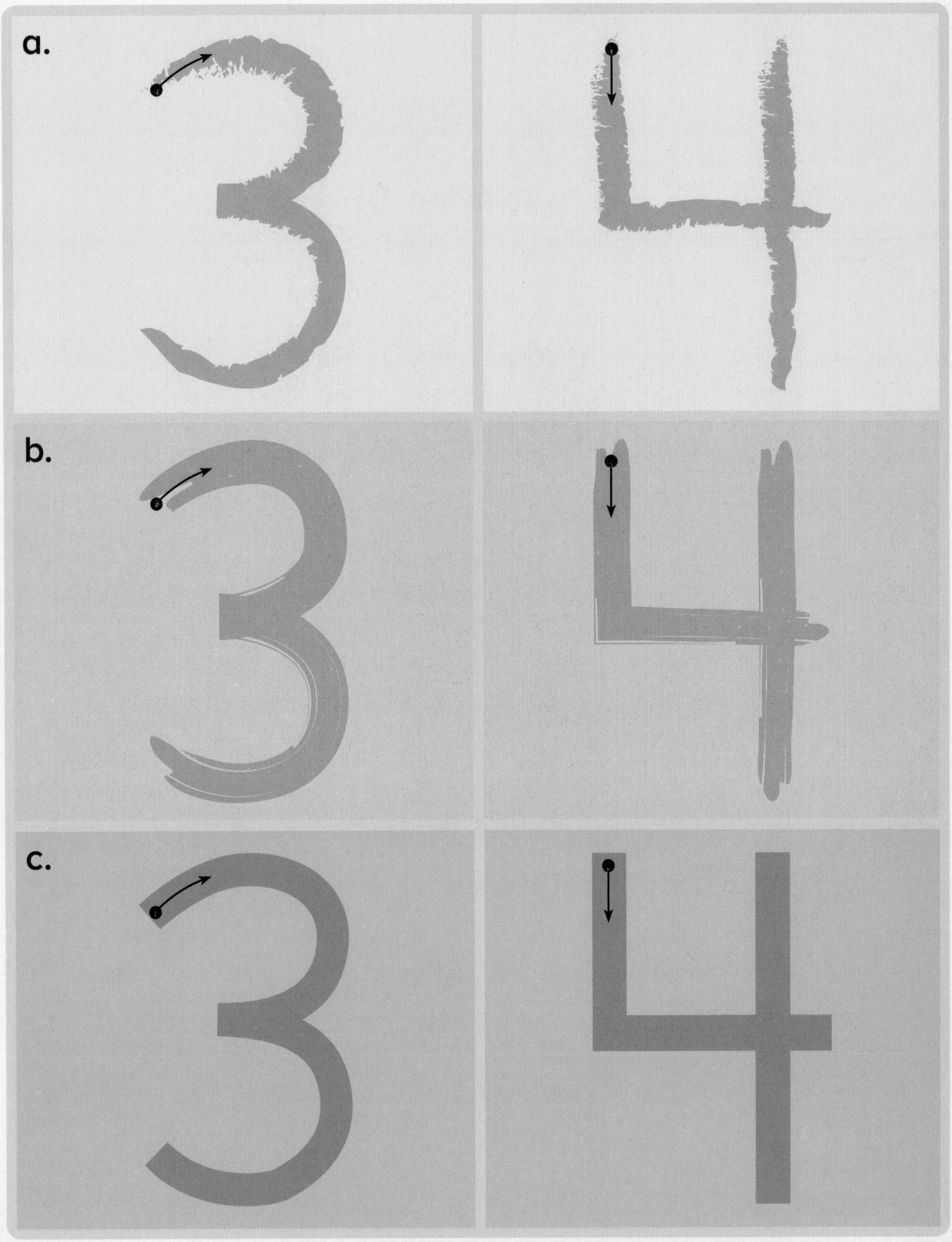

Have the student say each number aloud, then trace over the numeral with their finger and write it three times.

© ORIGO Education

a.	b.	c.	d.	e.
5	7	3	6	4

f.

1	2	3	4	5	6	7	8	9	10

just before

5	8	10	2	6

© ORIGO Education

Have the student draw ◯ to match the number, then write the numbers that come just before.

a. 10

b. 8

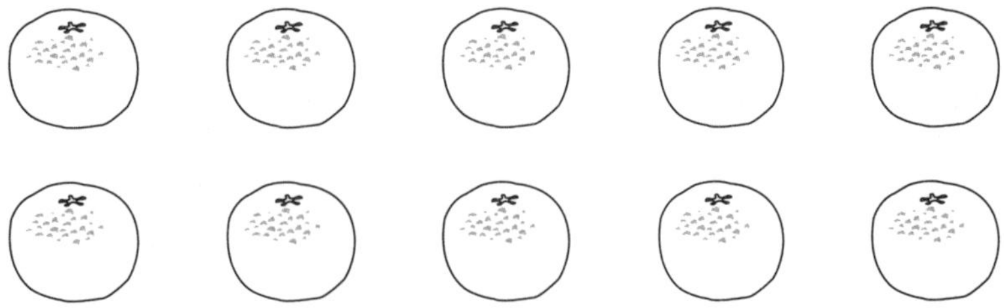

c. 6

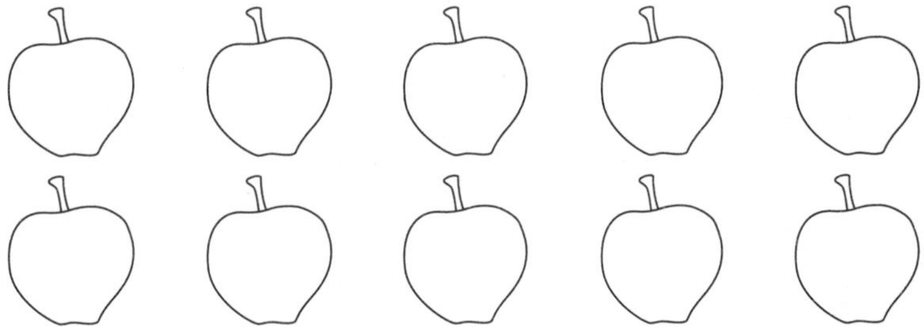

d. 9

e. 7

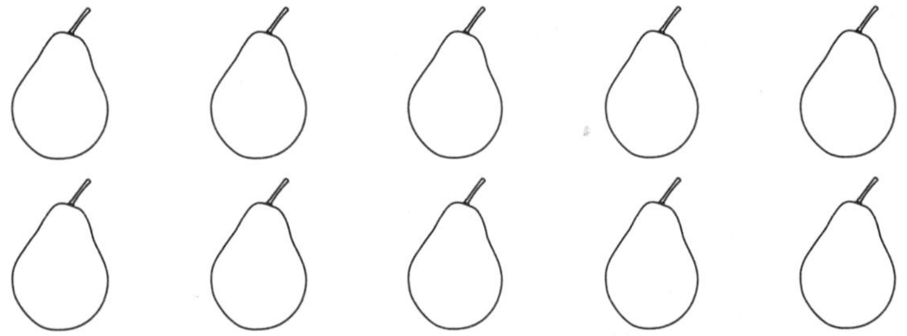

© ORIGO Education

Have the student color pieces of fruit to match each numeral. Then ask them to count the fruit aloud and say the matching number.

•	9	•• • ••
4	••• •••	1
8	• •	7
••• ••• •••	2	• • • •
• • •	5	3
••• • • •••	6	••• • •••

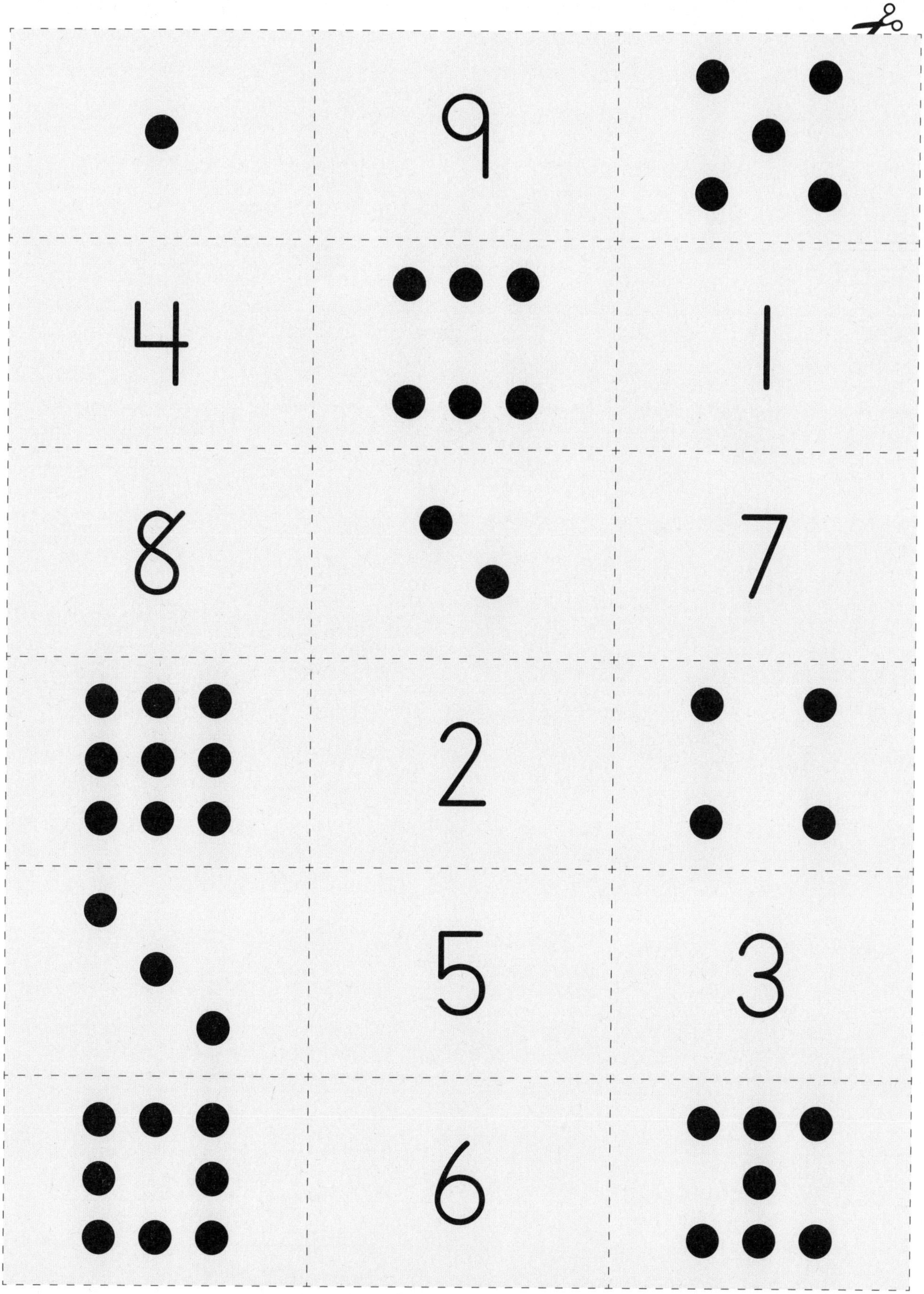

Have the student cut out the pictures and paste each quantity and its matching numeral back-to-back.

© ORIGO Education

a.

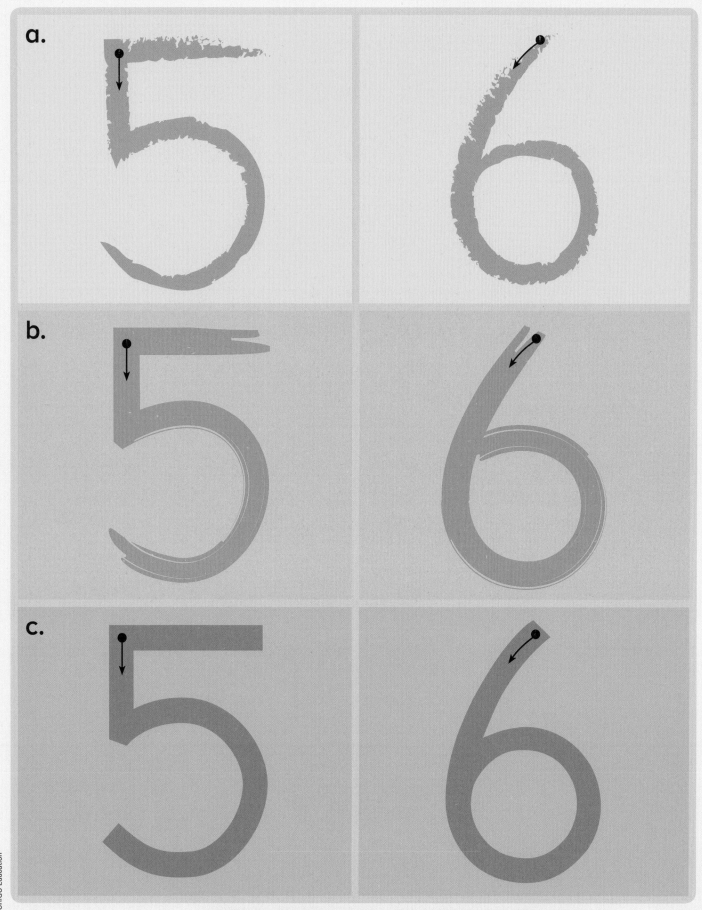

b.

c.

© ORIGO Education

Have the student say each number aloud, then trace over the numeral with their finger and write it three times.

a. 5

b. 2

c. 4

d. 6

e. 3

f. 1

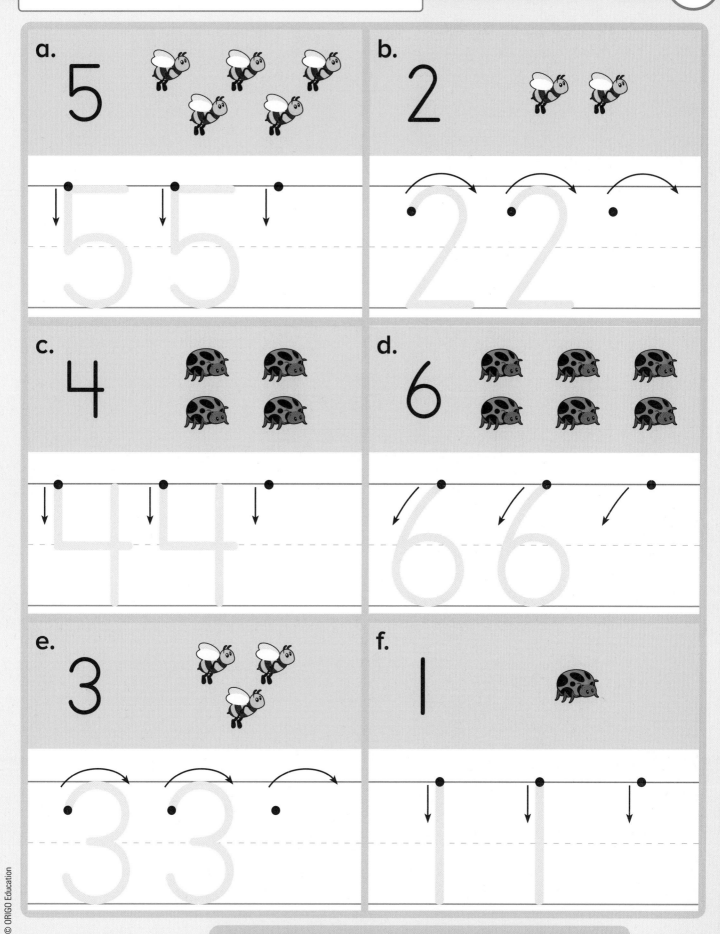

© ORIGO Education

Have the student count the bugs and say the number aloud, then follow the arrows to write the matching numeral.

a.

7

b.

8

c.

9

d.

10

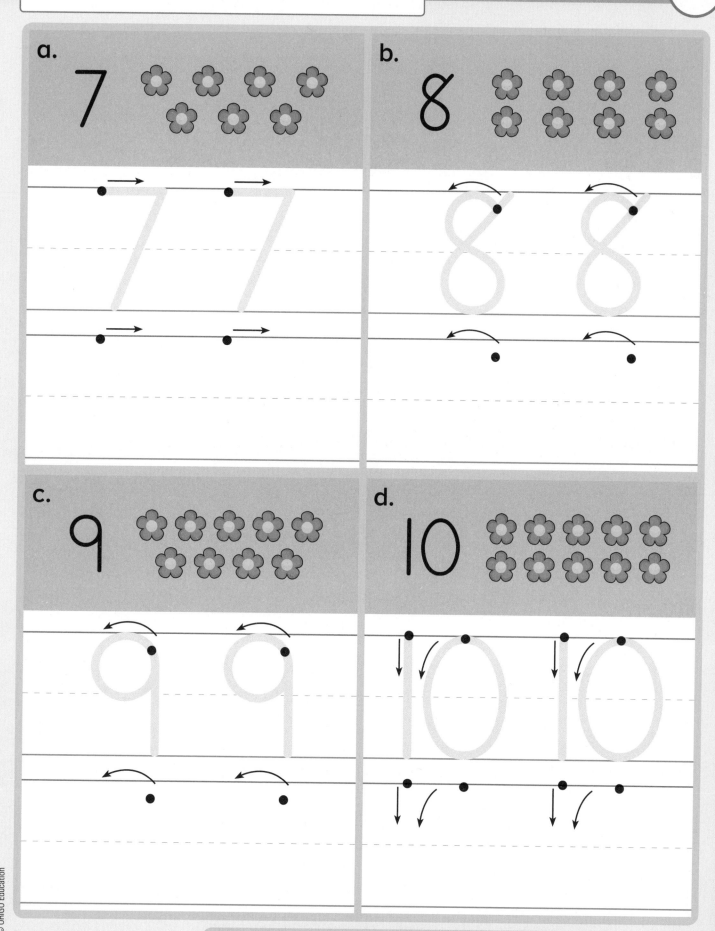

© ORIGO Education

Have the student count the flowers and say the number aloud, then follow the arrows to write the matching numeral.

a.

b.

c.

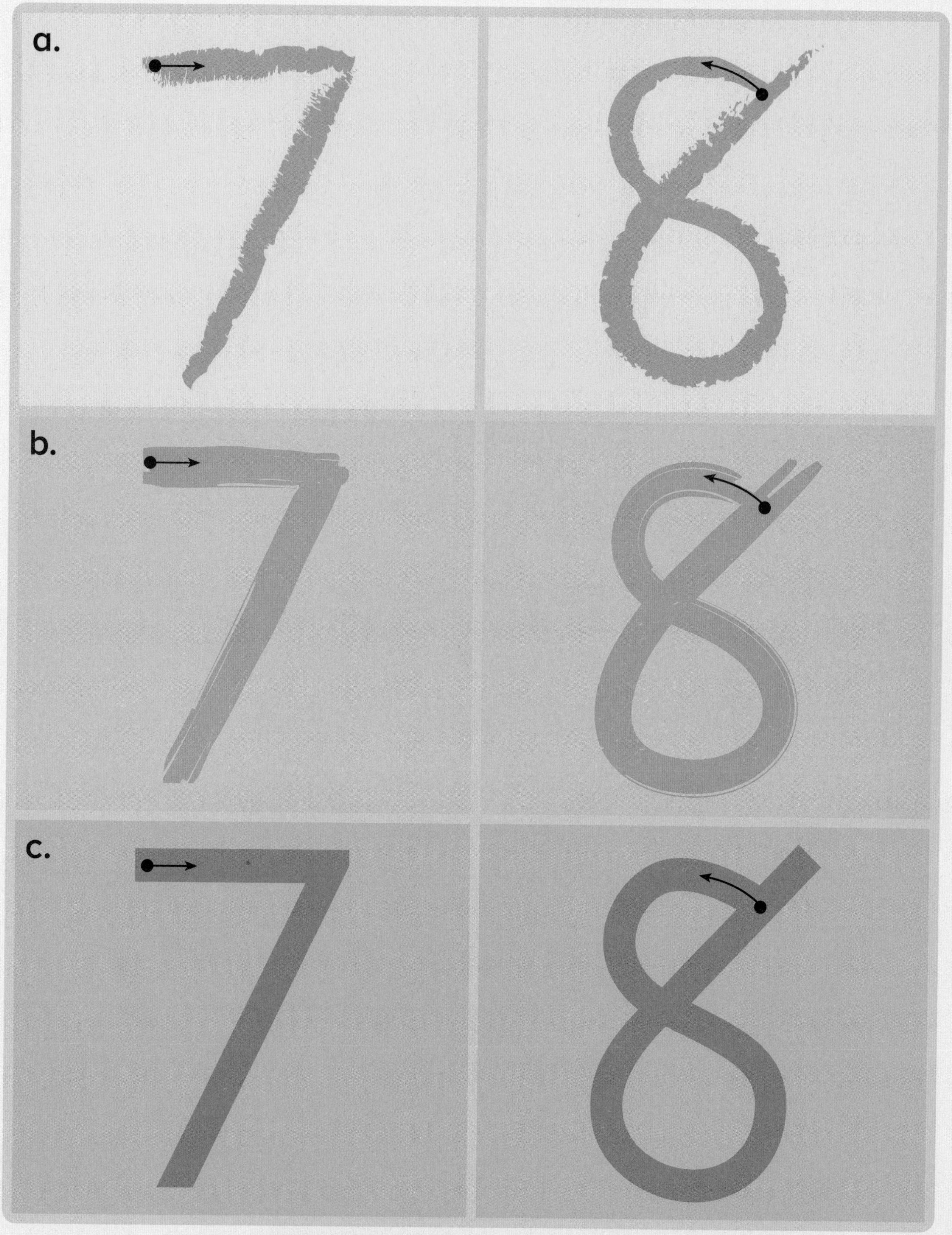

© ORIGO Education

Have the student say each number aloud, then trace over the numeral with their finger and write it three times.

1.

a.

1	2				6	7	8	9	10

b.

1	2	3	4				8	9	10

c.

			4	5	6	7	8	9	10

2.

a.

6		8		10

b.

2			5	6

c.

	4	5		7

d.

	6	7	8	

© ORIGO Education

Have the student work left to right to trace over the gray numerals and write the missing numbers on each blue number track. Then have the student write the numbers that are missing on each pink number track part.

1	2	3	4	5	6	7	8	9

a.

just before

6 7   4   9   6   3

6				
7	4	9	6	3

b.

just after

2	8	5	6	3
3				

© ORIGO Education

Have the student trace over the words then write the appropriate numbers.
They can use the number track to help.

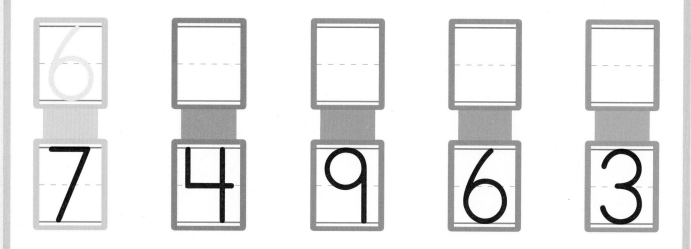

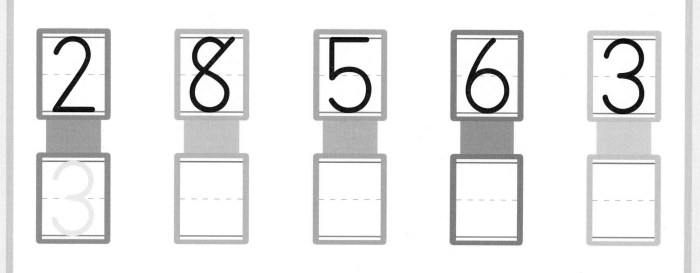

a.

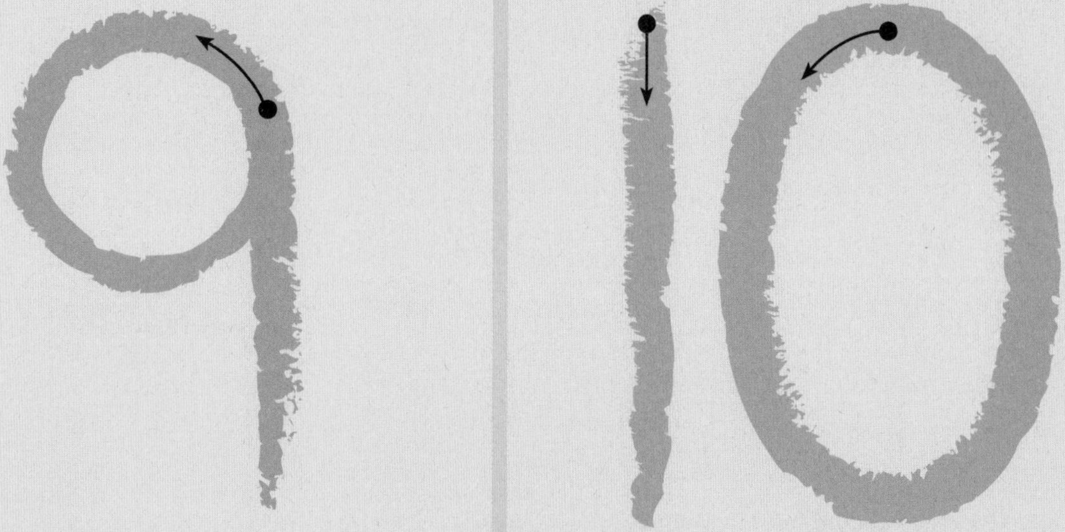

b.

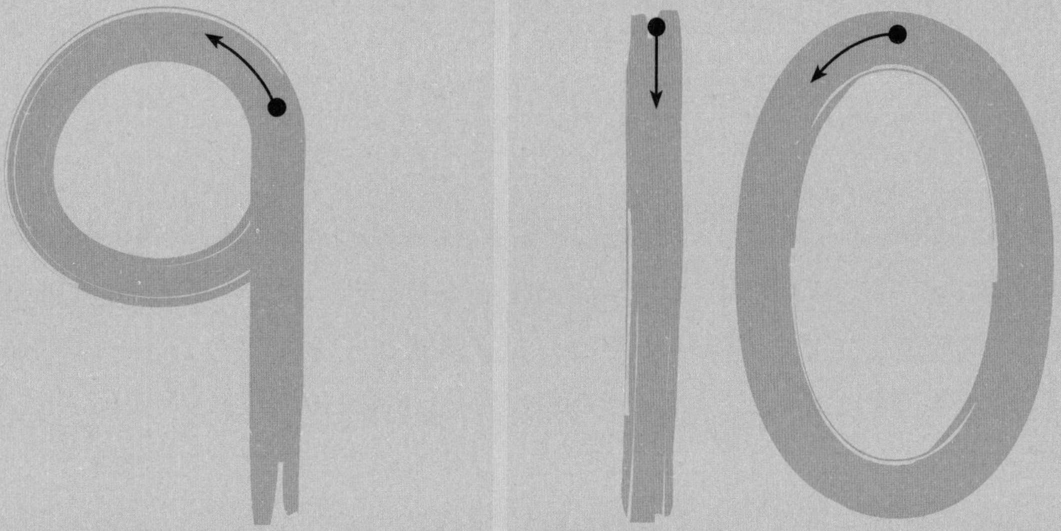

c.

Have the student say each number aloud, then trace over the numeral with their finger and write it three times.

© ORIGO Education

a.

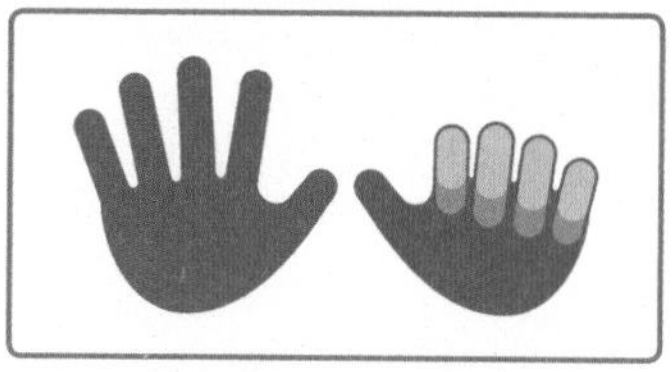

b.

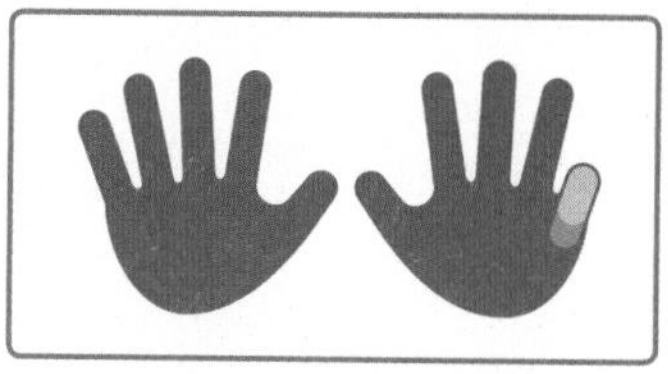

c.

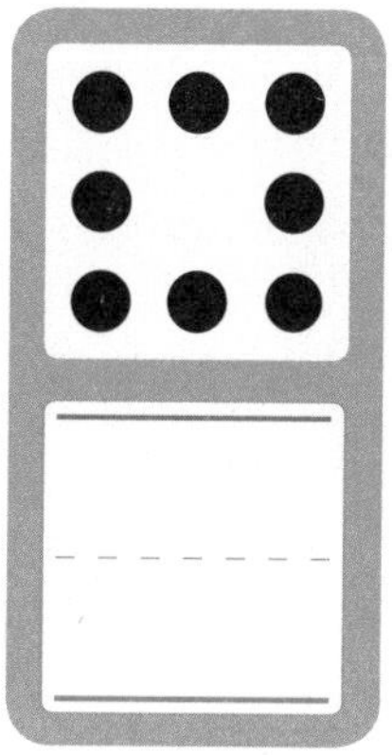

d.

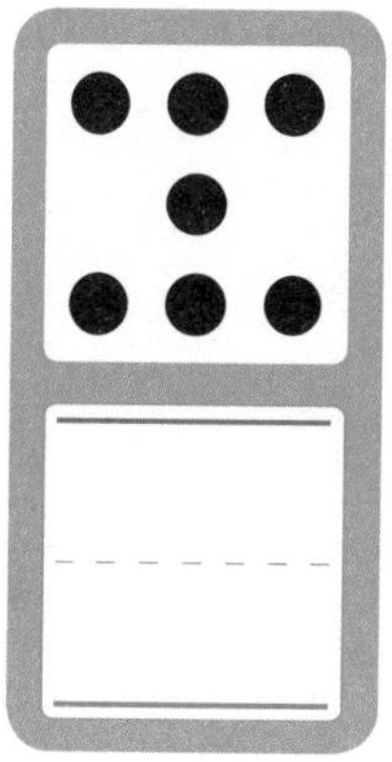

e.

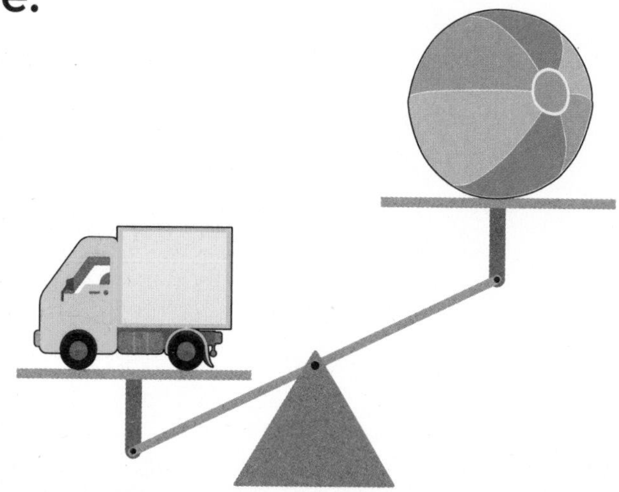

f.

© ORIGO Education

Have the student write the numbers of raised fingers then circle the greater number. Repeat this for the dominoes. Then have the student circle the toys that are heavier.

fewer		more
	a. 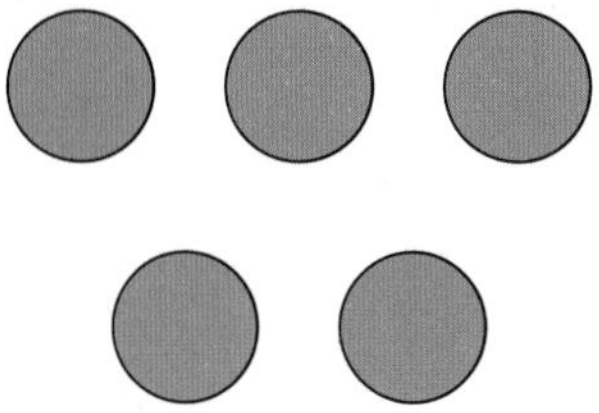	
	b. 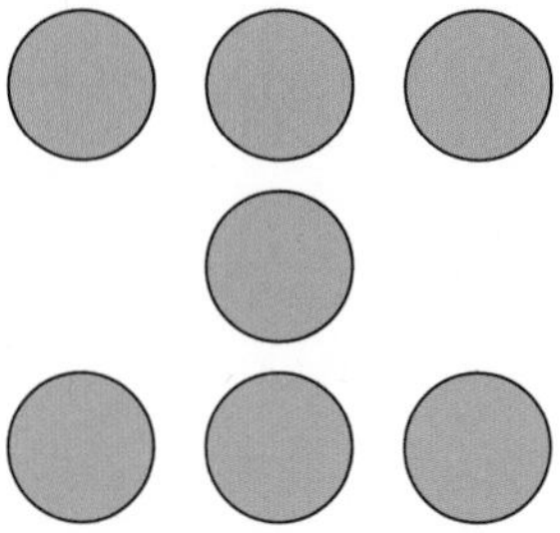	
	c. 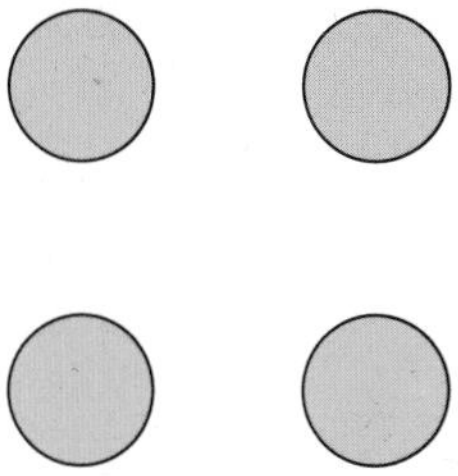	
	d. 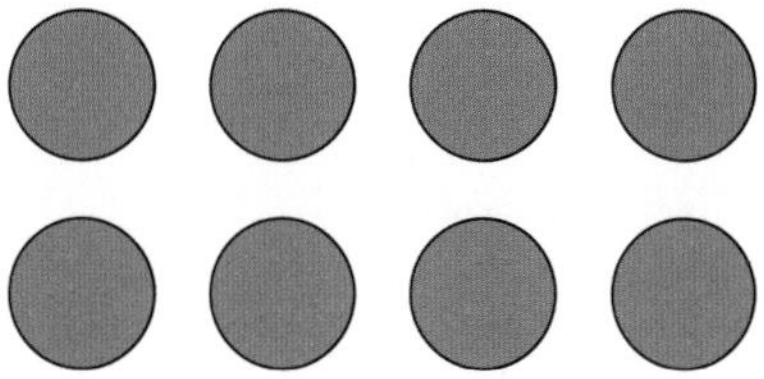	
	e. 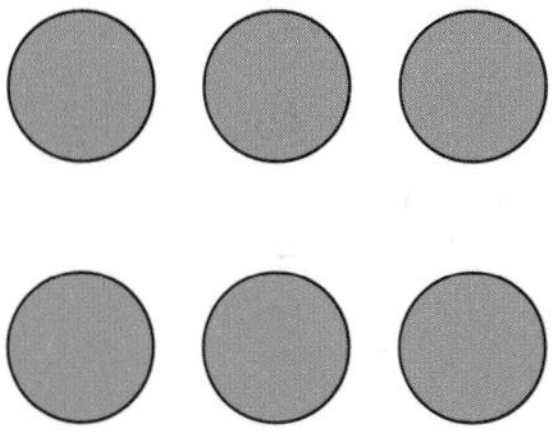	

Have the student say the number in each group, then draw ◯ to show groups that have **fewer** and **more**.

© ORIGO Education

a.

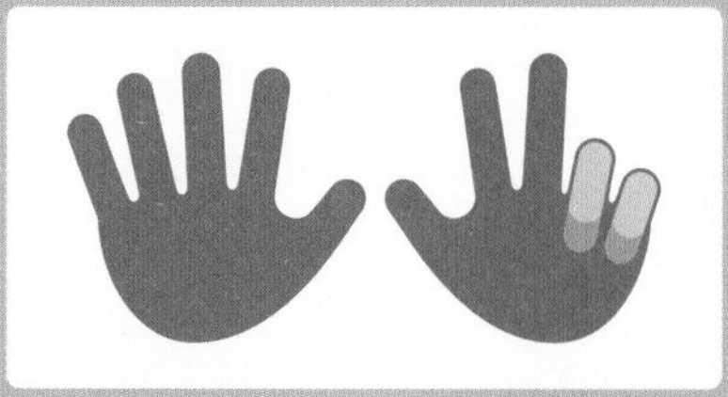

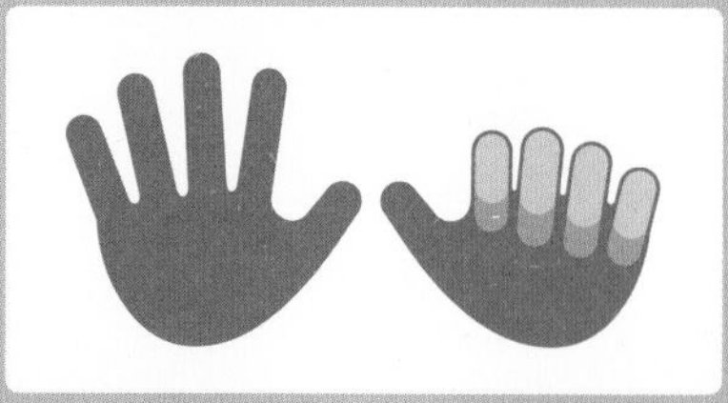

b.

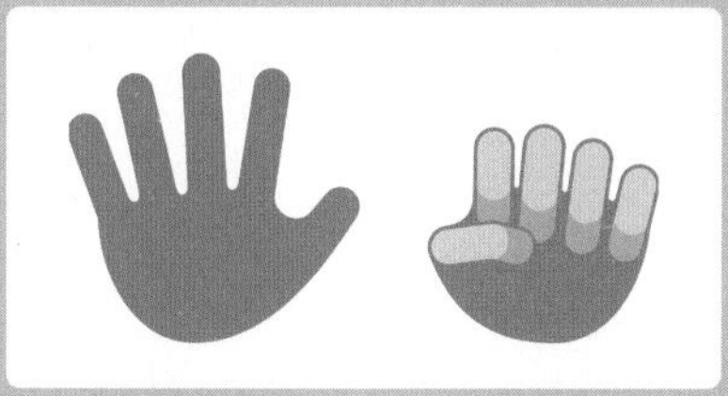

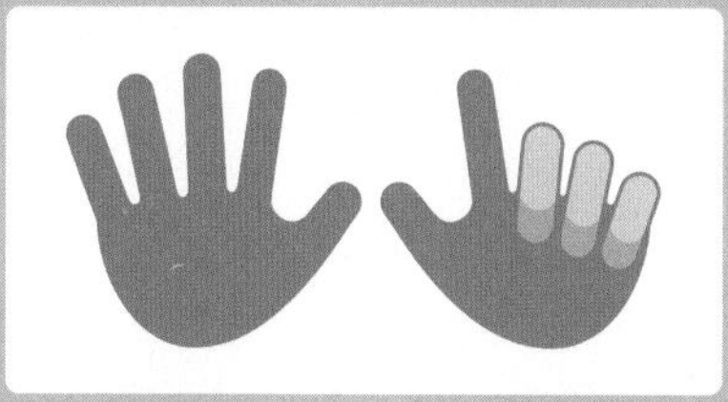

c.

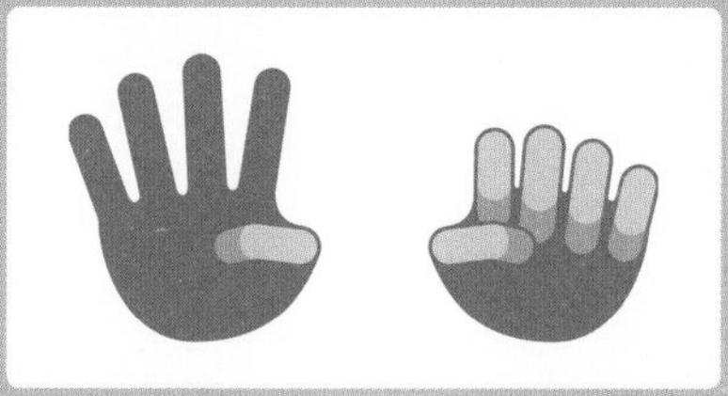

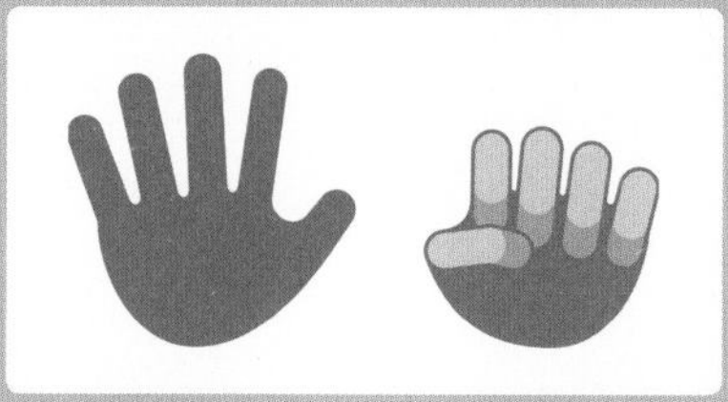

d.

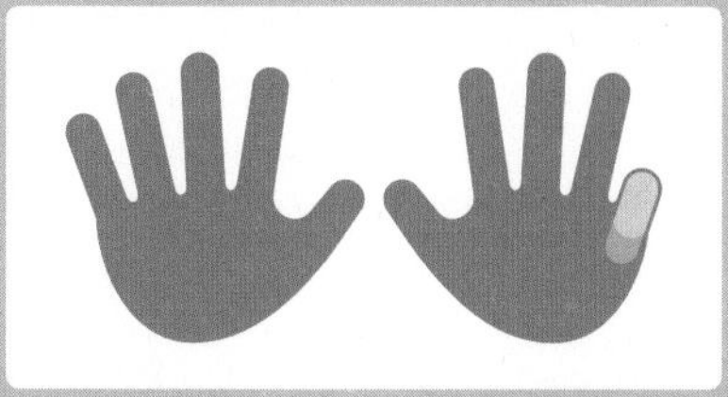

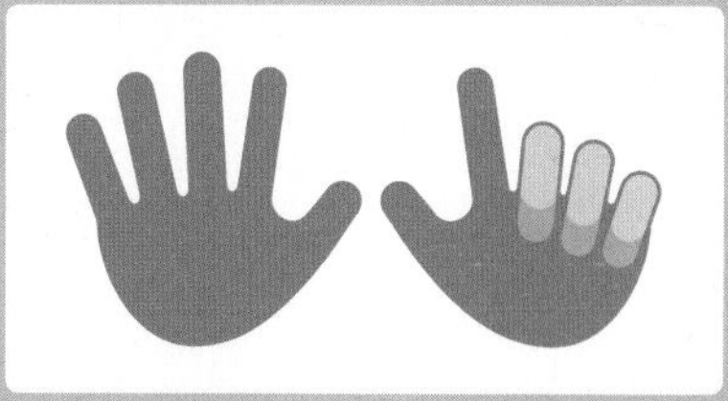

© ORIGO Education

For each puzzle, have the student write the number of fingers raised, then circle the group that has fewer.

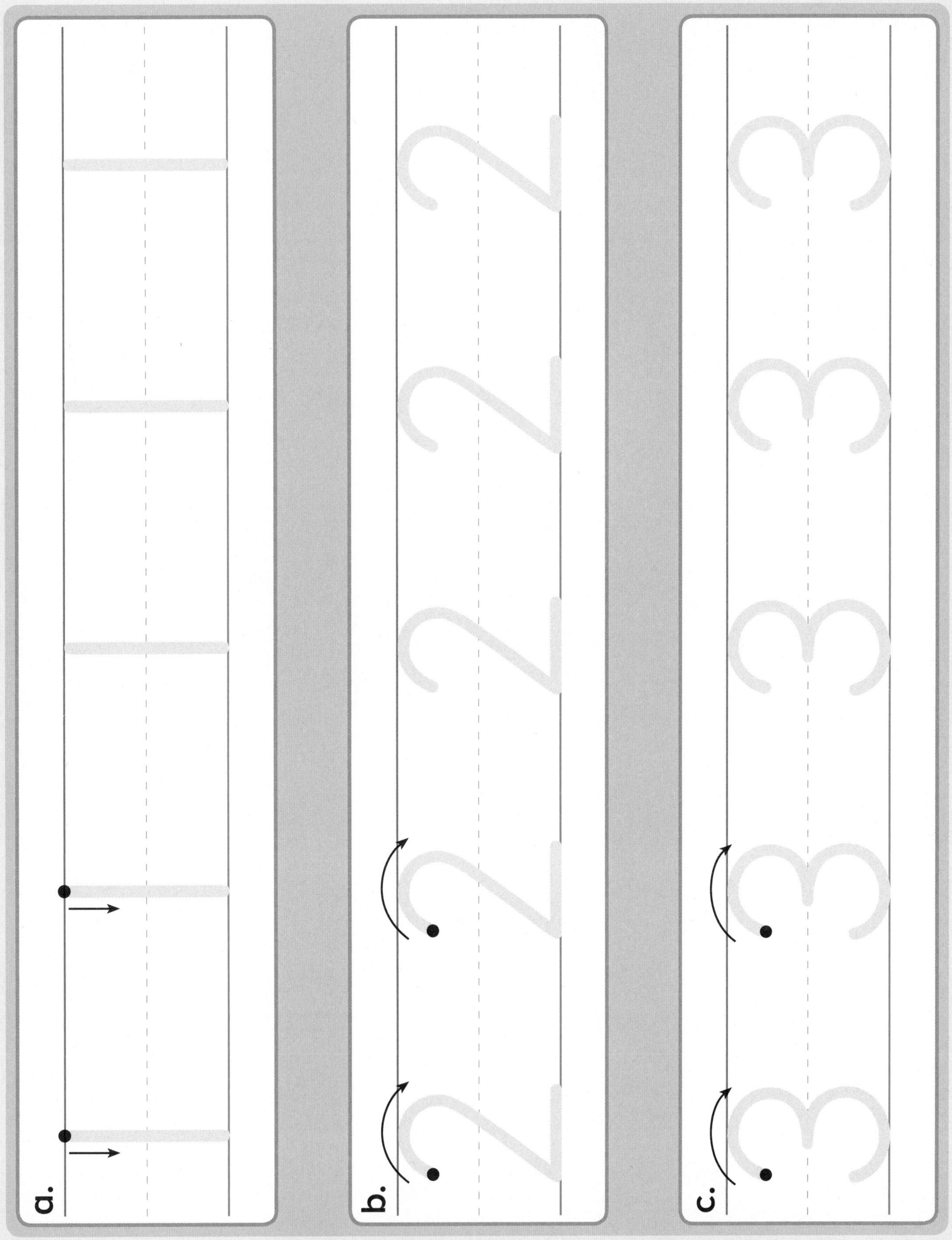

For each of these, have the student say the number aloud, then trace the numeral five times.

© ORIGO Education

6 3

2 5

4 9

9 6

7 1

6 7

6 8

1 3

5 4

9 8

© ORIGO Education

Have the student read aloud the two numbers on a card then color the numeral that represents the greater number. Repeat for all.

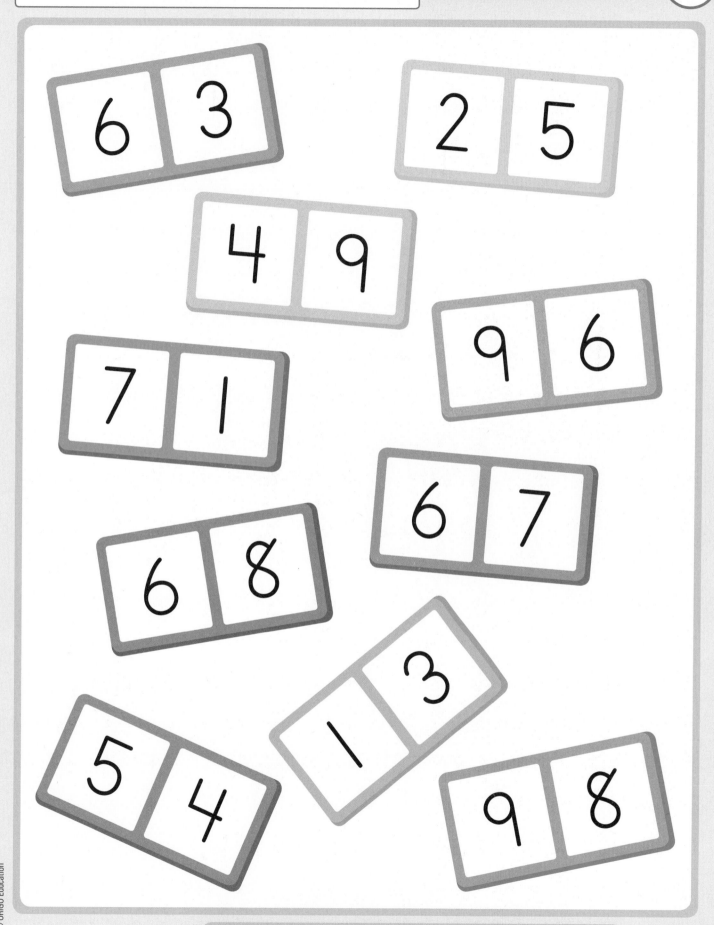

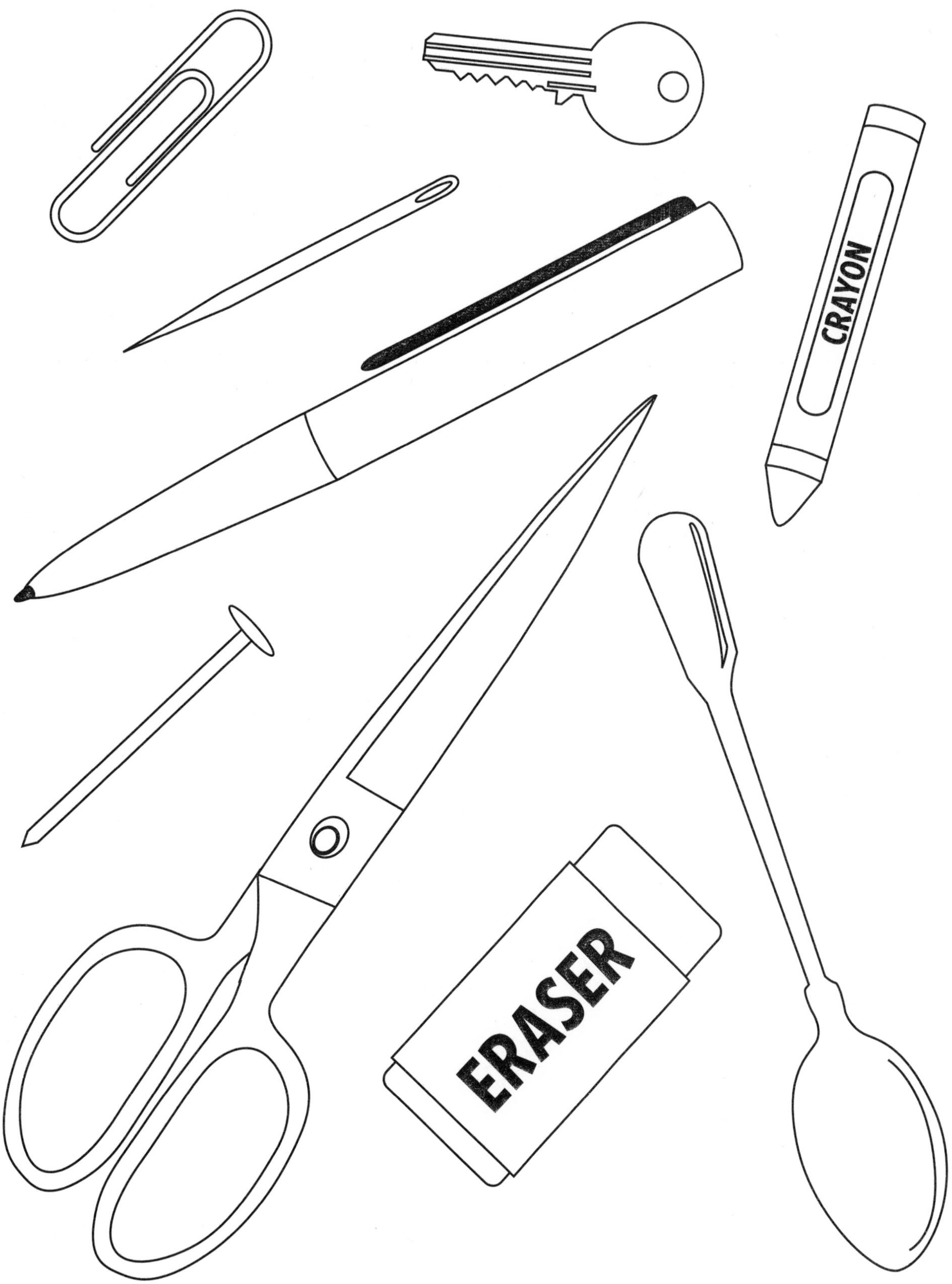

© ORIGO Education

Cut a piece of string 4 inches long. Have the student compare the string to each picture, then color the pictures blue that are shorter and color the pictures red that are longer.

a. 2 2 2 2 2

b. 3 3 3 3 3

c. 4 4 4 4 4

For each of these, have the student say the number aloud, then trace the numeral five times.

© ORIGO Education

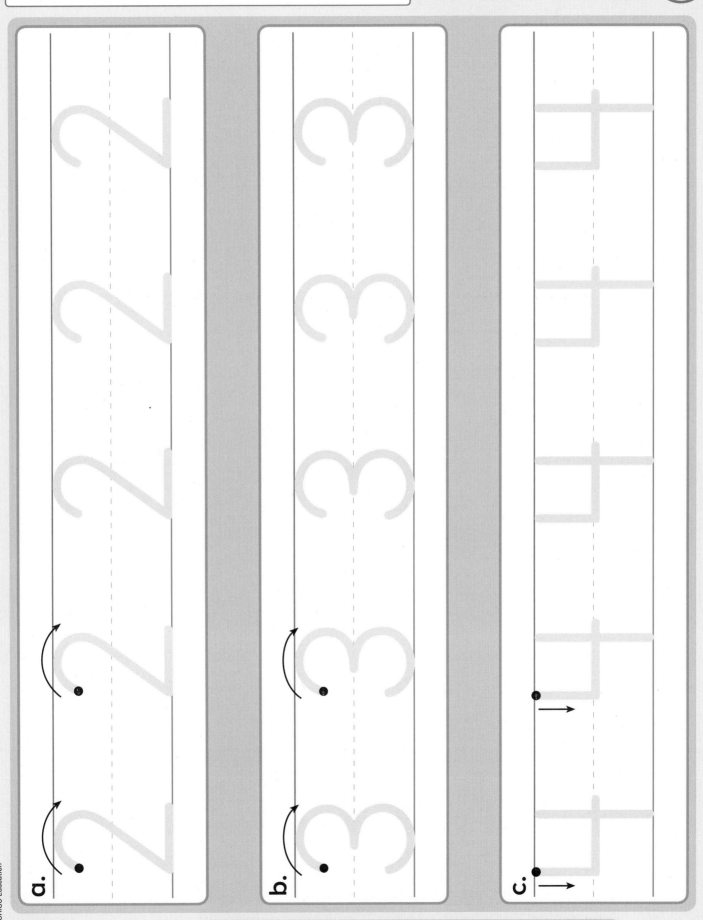

a.

b.

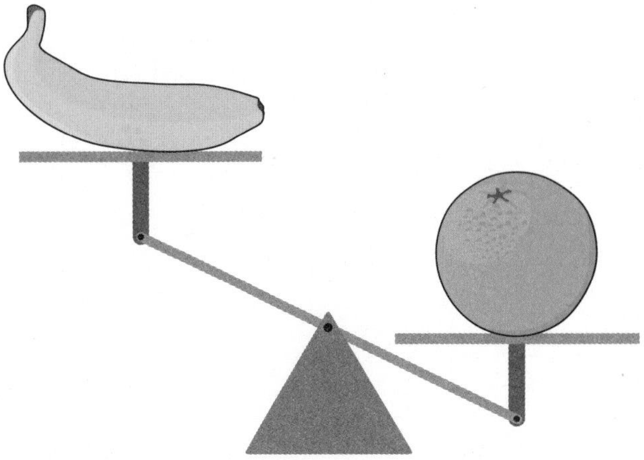

c.

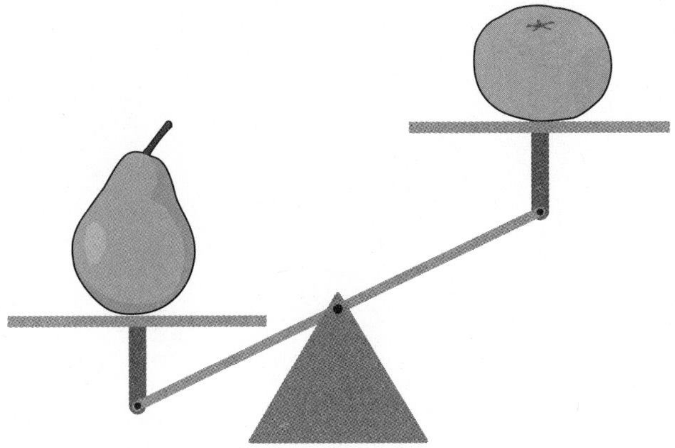

d.

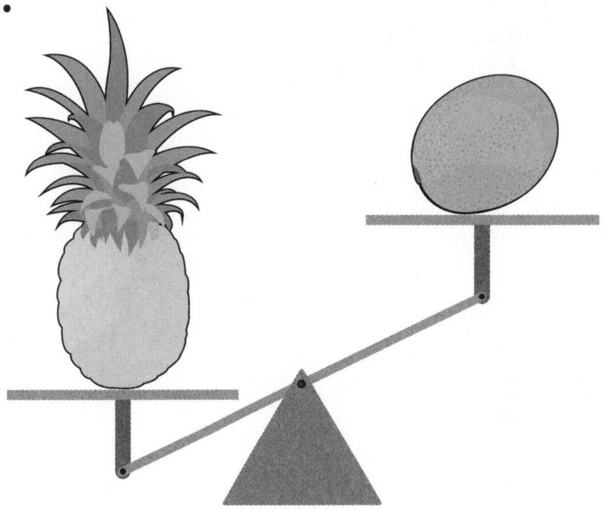

e.

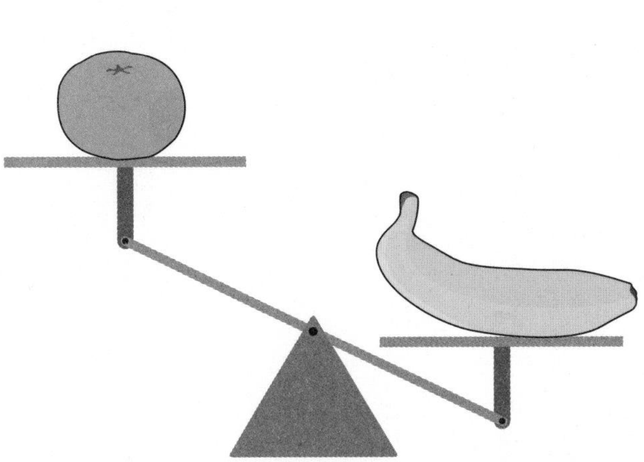

f.

For each balance, have the student circle the fruit that is heavier.

© ORIGO Education

a.

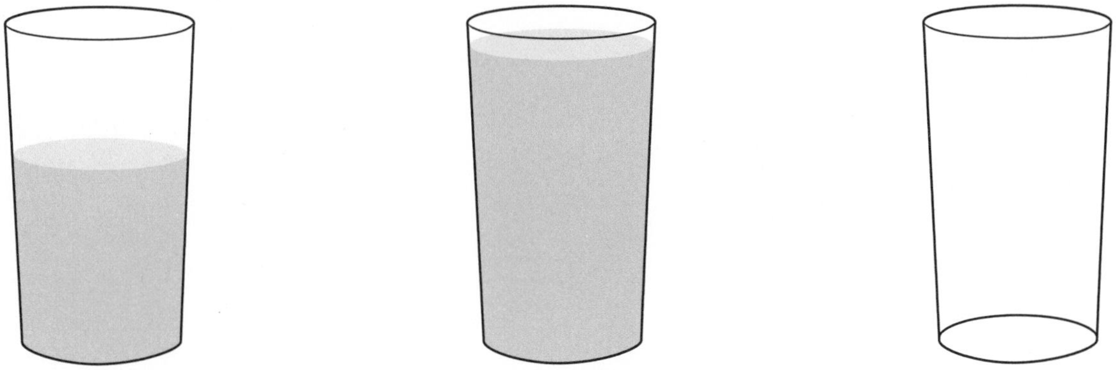

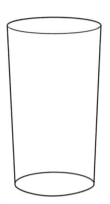

full | half full | empty

b.

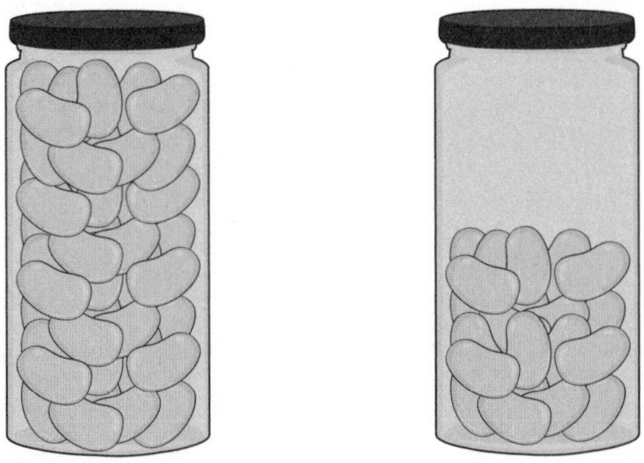

c.

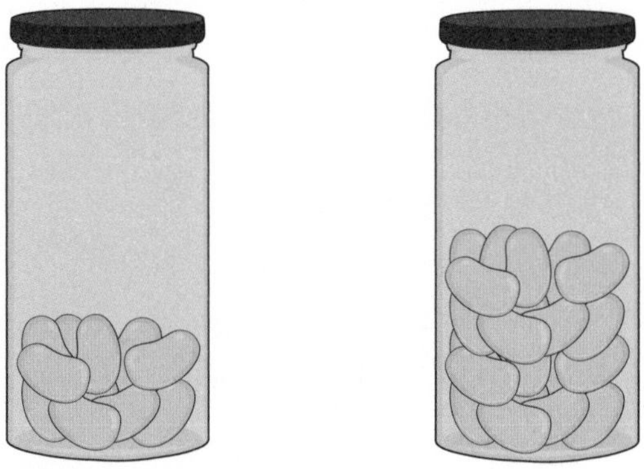

© ORIGO Education

Have the student draw a line from each glass to a matching label. Then, for each pair of jars, have the student circle the one that is holding more beans.

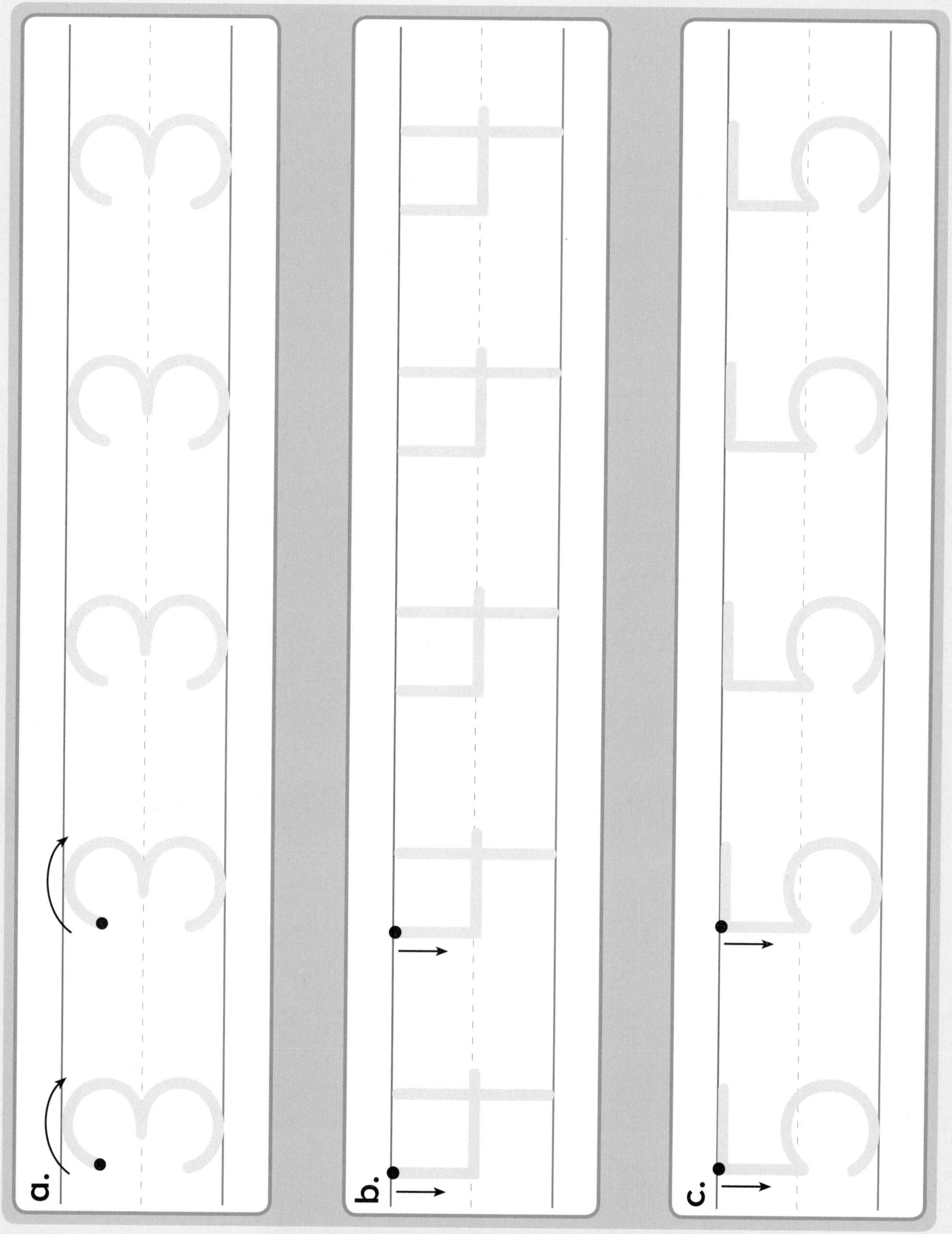

© ORIGO Education

For each of these, have the student say the number aloud, then trace the numeral five times.

a. 6 six

six

b. 9 nine

nine

c.

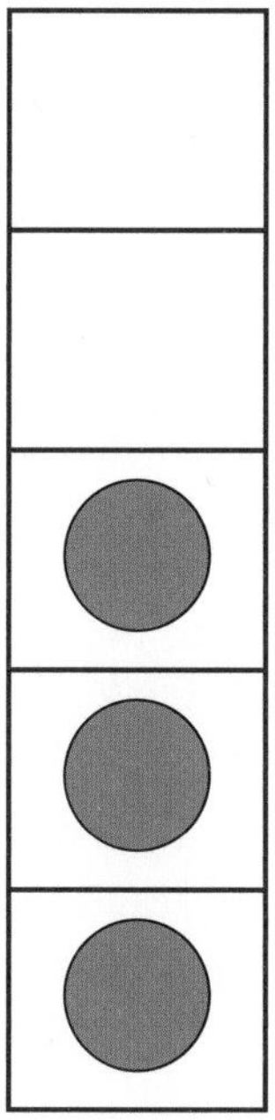

d.

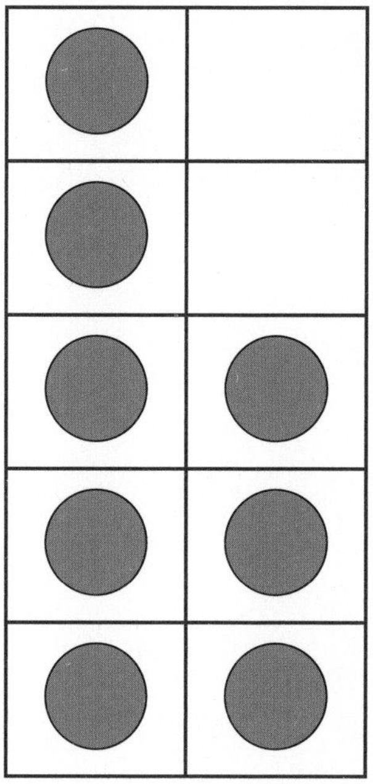

e.

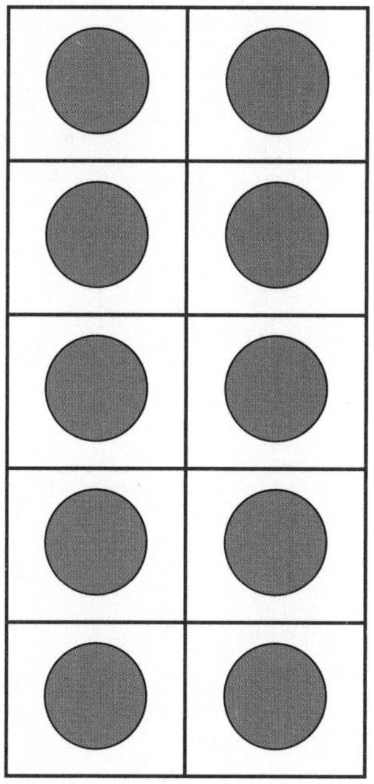

© ORIGO Education

Ask the student to read the number and number name, then have the student write the number name and draw ◯ to match the number represented. Next have the student write the numerals to match the number of dots.

a. 6 six

b. 3 three

c. 10 ten

d. 7 seven

e. 0 zero

© ORIGO Education

Ask the student to read the number and number name, then have the student write the number name and draw ◯ to match the number represented.

a. 2	two		
b. 4	four		
c. 8	eight		
d. 9	nine		
e. 5	five		
f. 1	one		

© ORIGO Education

Ask the student to read the numeral and number name, then have the student write the number name and draw ◯ to match the number represented.

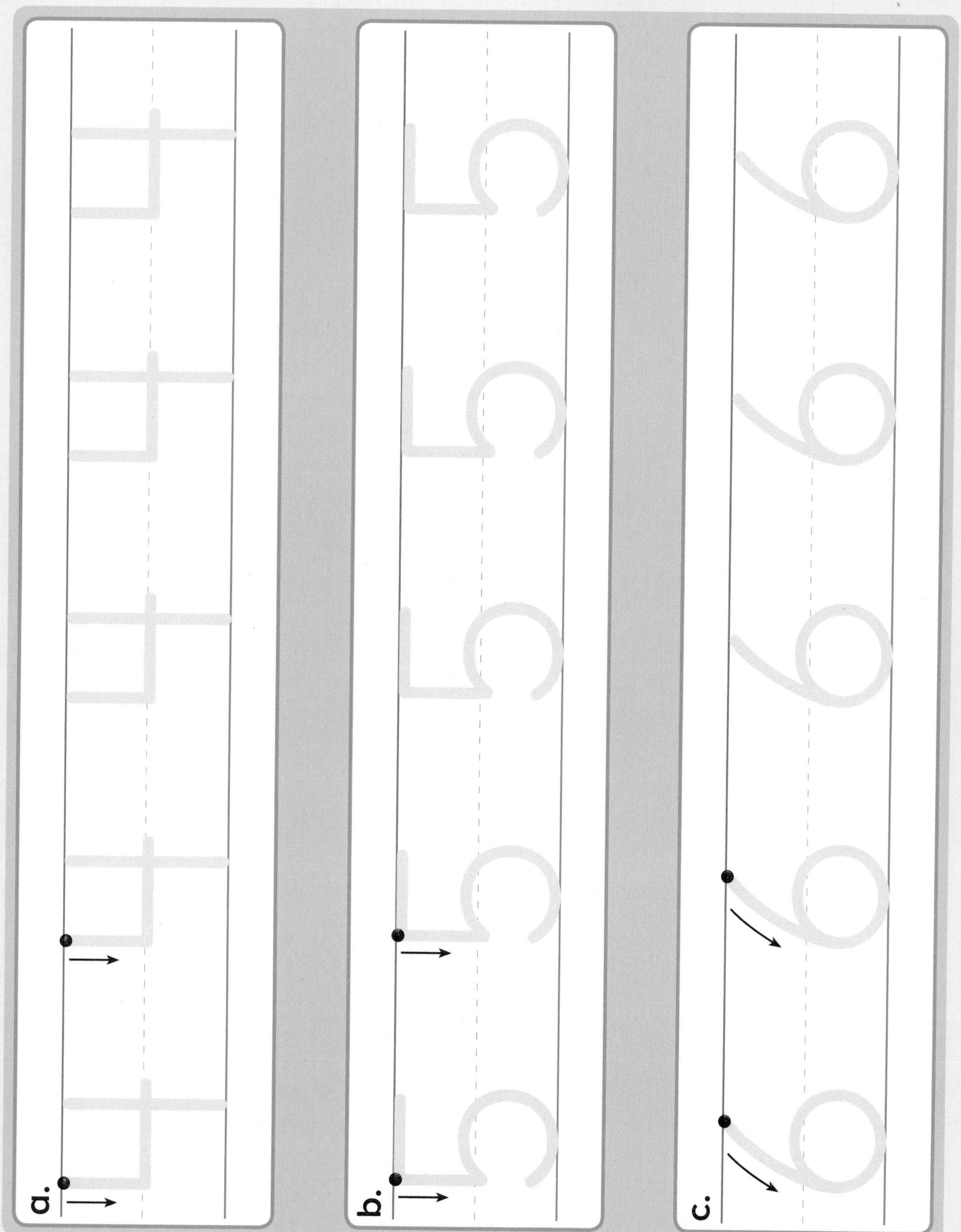

For each of these, have the student say the number aloud, then trace the numeral five times.

© ORIGO Education

four	seven	ten
one	zero	three
six	five	eight
nine	two	

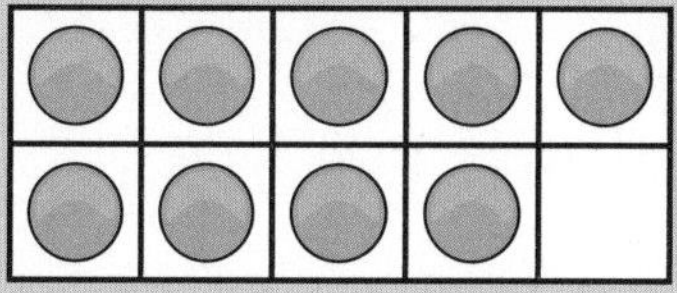
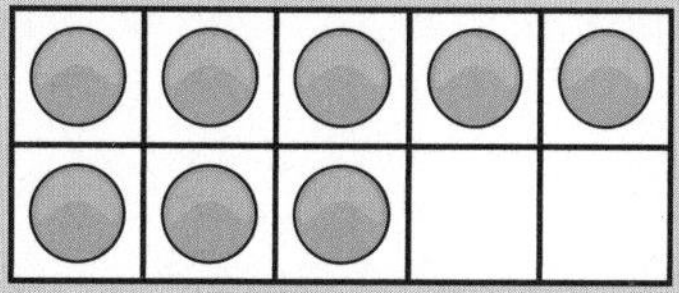
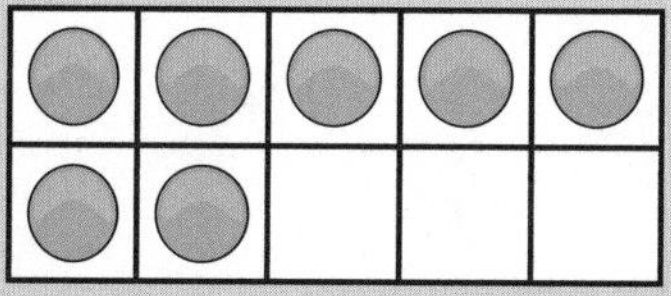
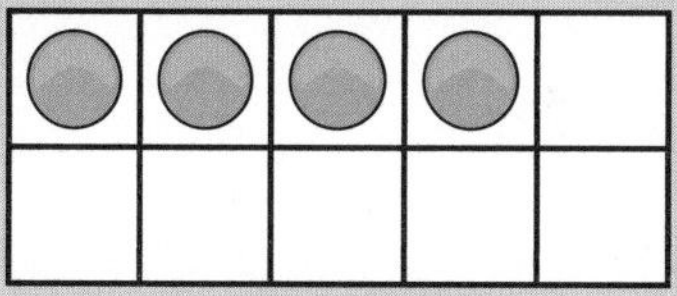
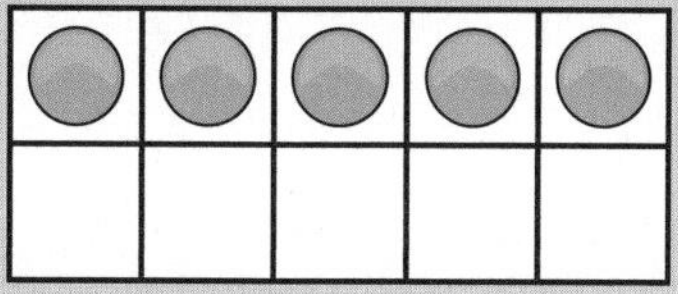
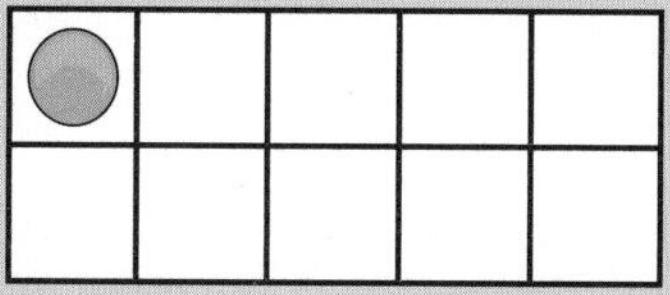
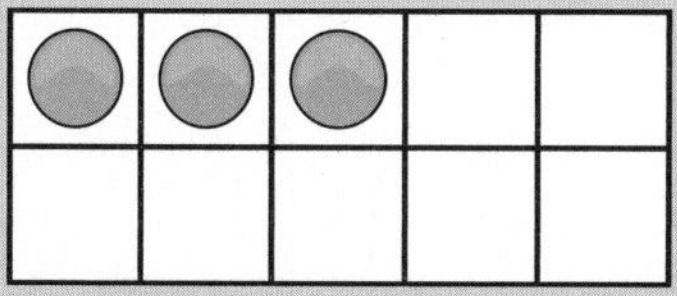
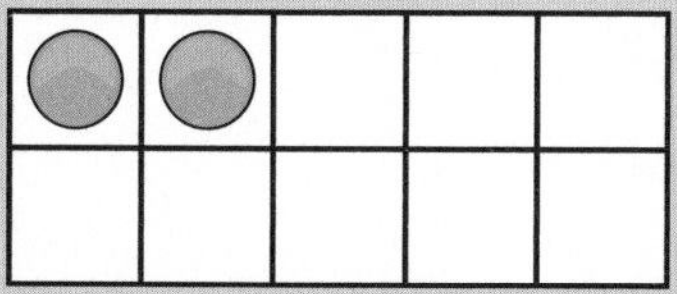
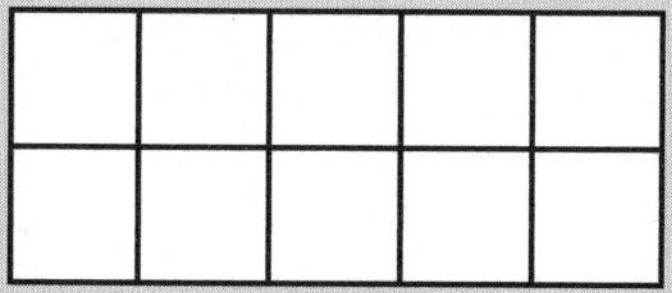
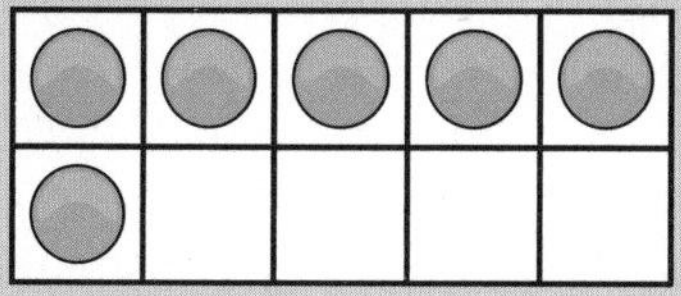
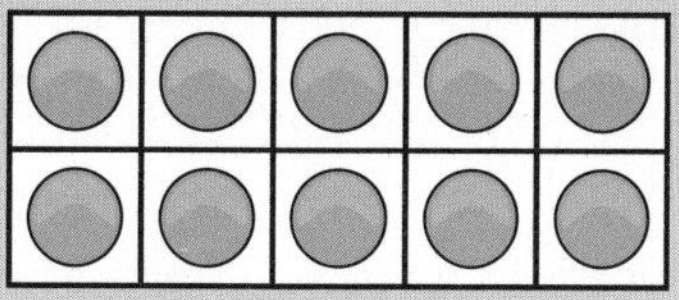

© ORIGO Education

Have the student cut out the pictures, paste matching pairs together on a sheet of paper, and write the matching numeral for each pair.

a.
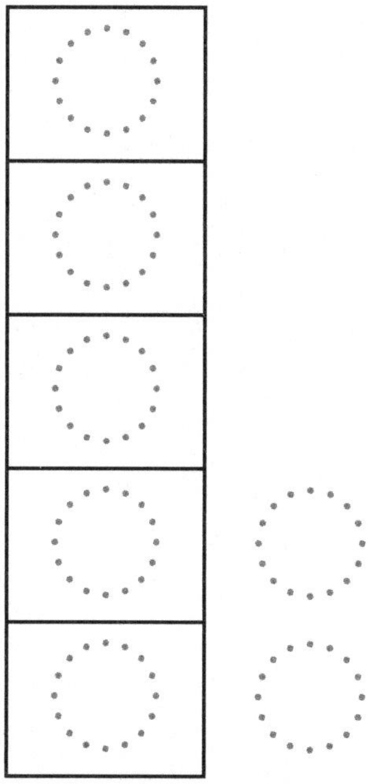

b.
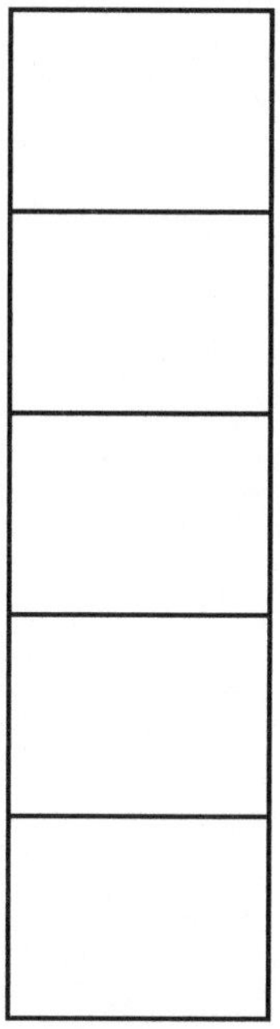

c.
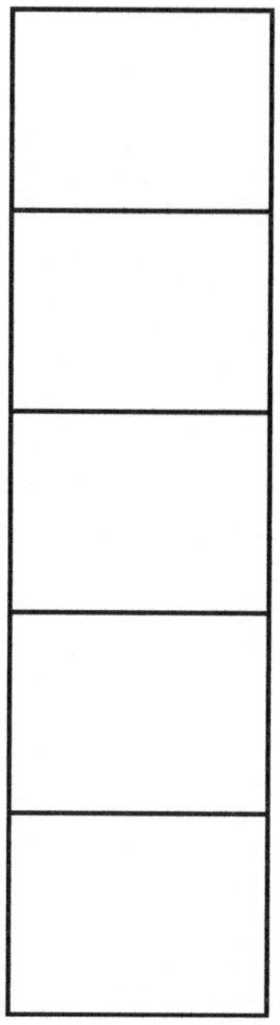

7

5

9

d.
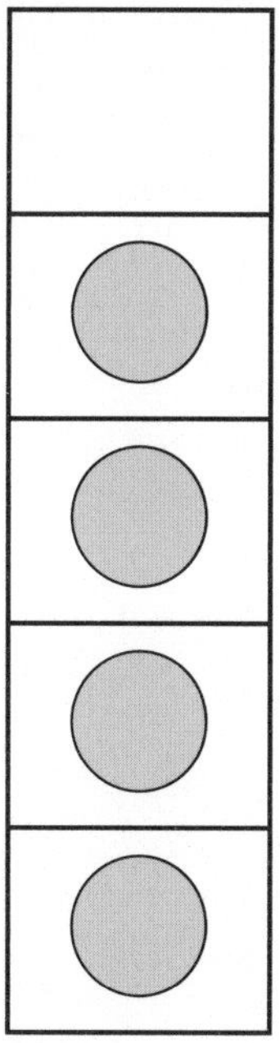

e.
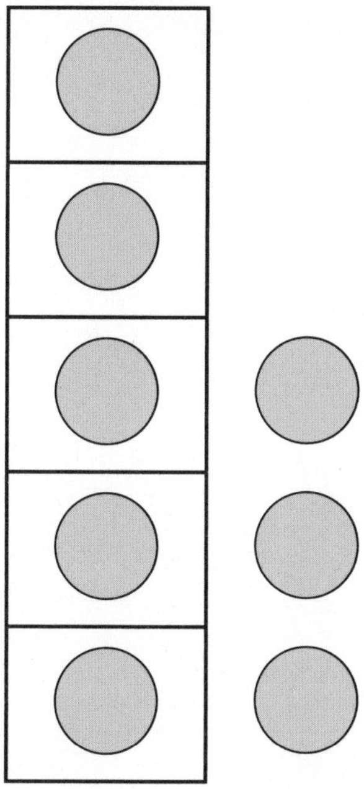

f.
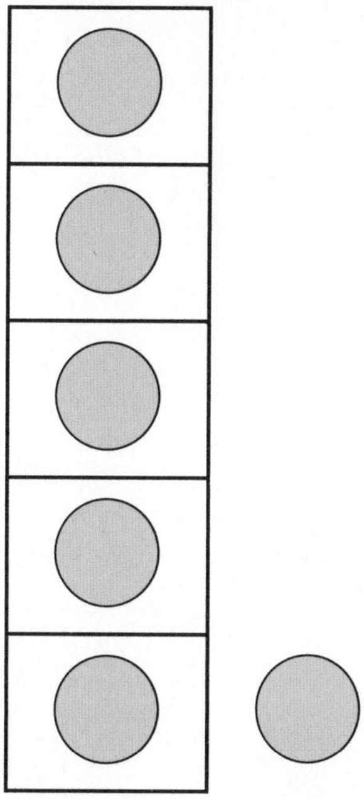

© ORIGO Education

Have the student draw ◯ to match the numeral, filling in the five-frame first. Ask the student to describe each example using language such as "Seven is five and two more." Then have the student write the numeral to match the number represented.

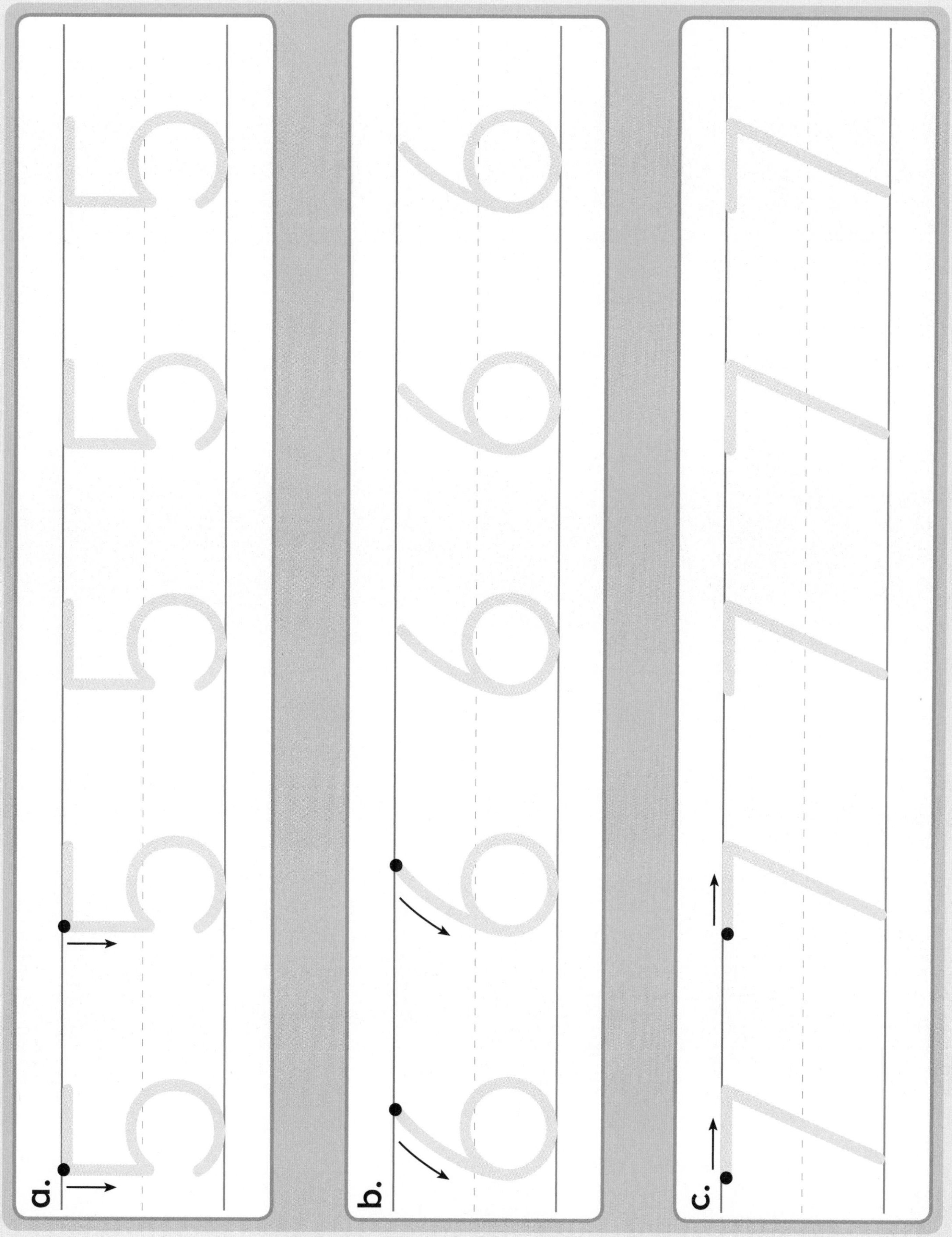

© ORIGO Education

For each of these, have the student say the number aloud, then trace the numeral five times.

a.

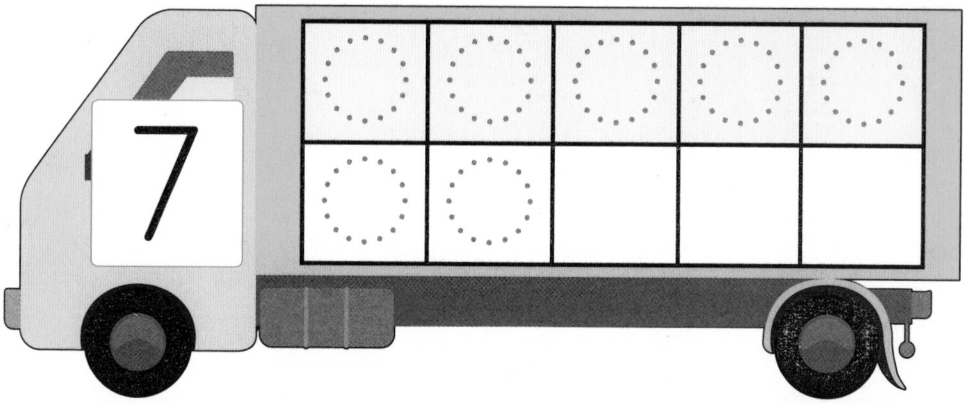

b.

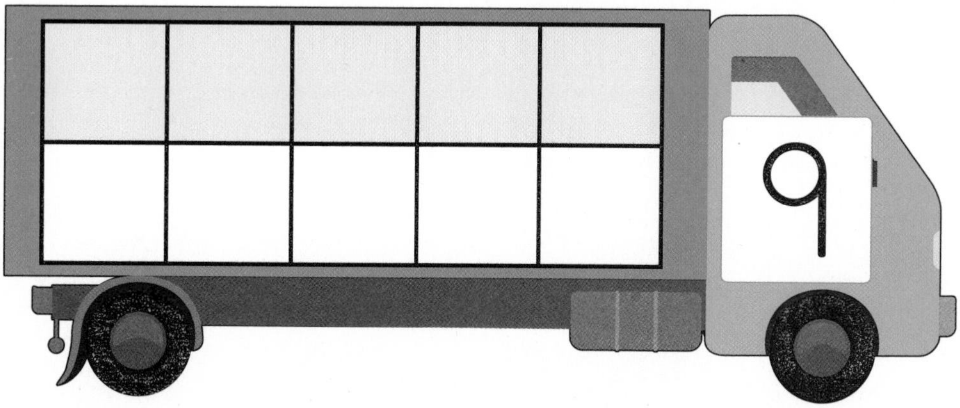

c.

d.

© ORIGO Education

Have the student draw ◯ on each ten-frame to match the numeral on the trucks. Then have the student write the numeral to match the number represented by the ten-frame on each train.

a.

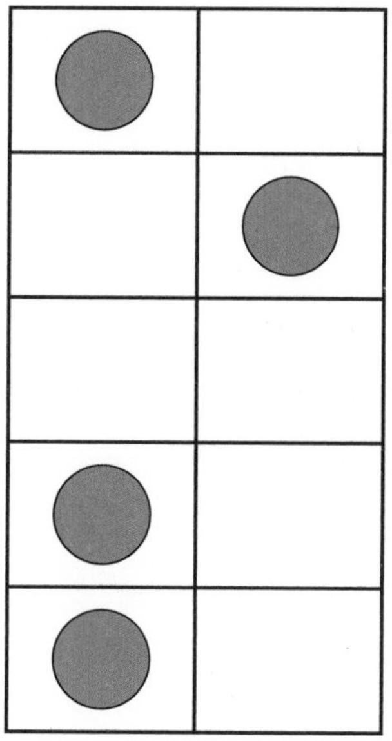

b.

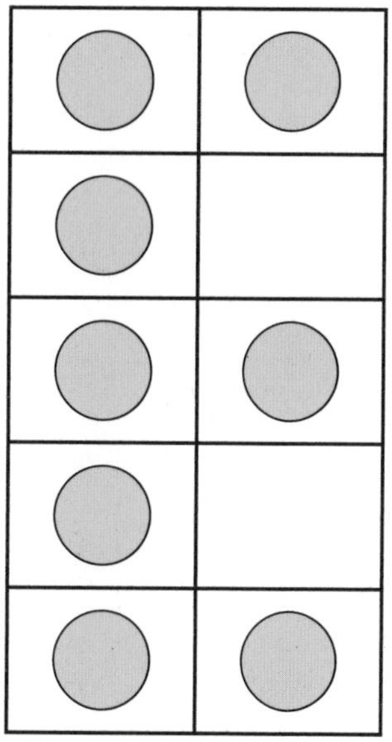

c.

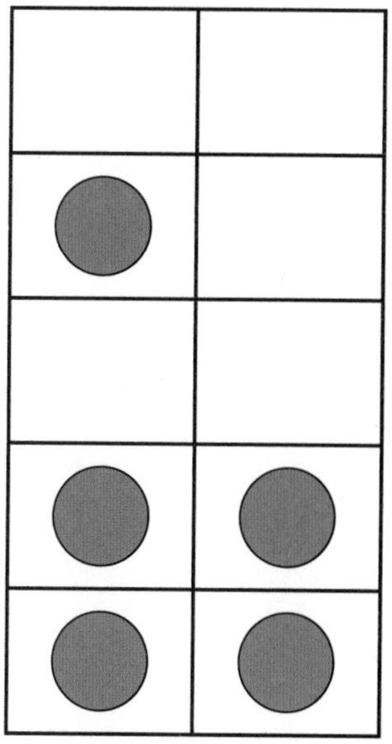

d.

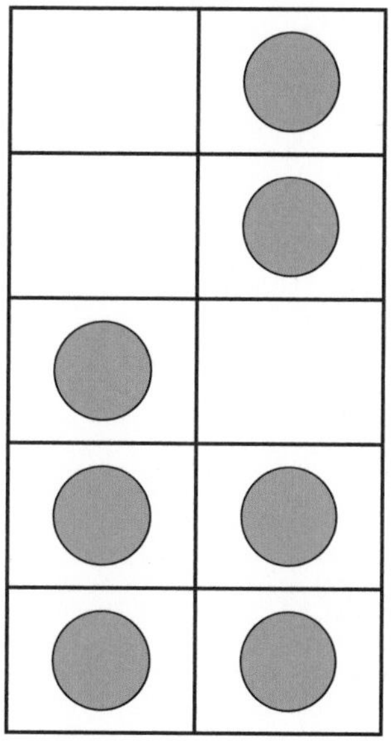

e.

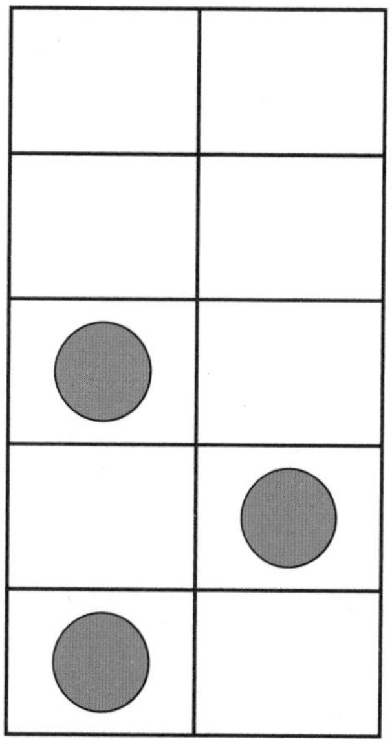

f.

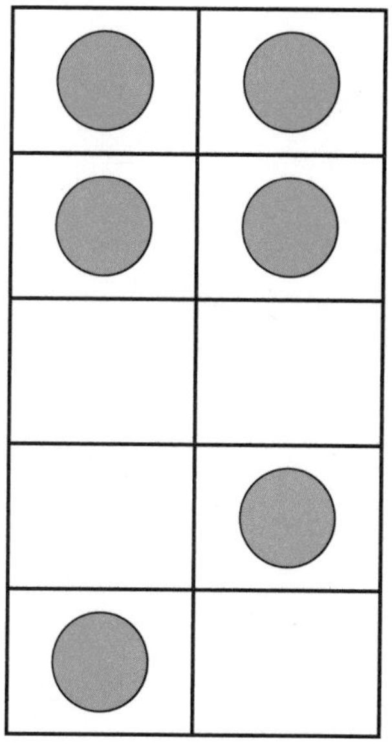

© ORIGO Education

Have the student look at the dots on the ten-frame and then write the numeral to match the number represented.

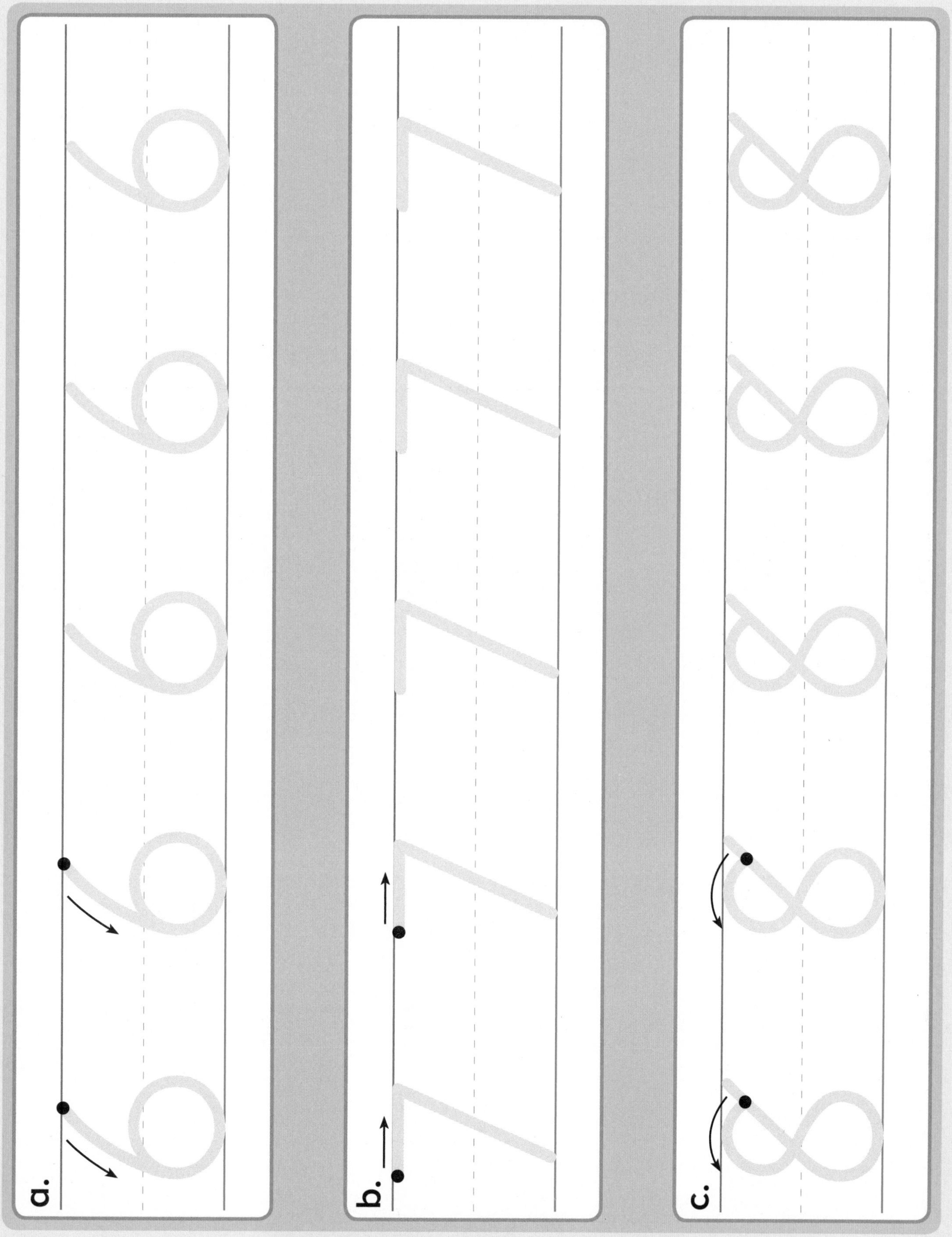

For each of these, have the student say the number aloud, then trace the numeral five times.

© ORIGO Education

a.

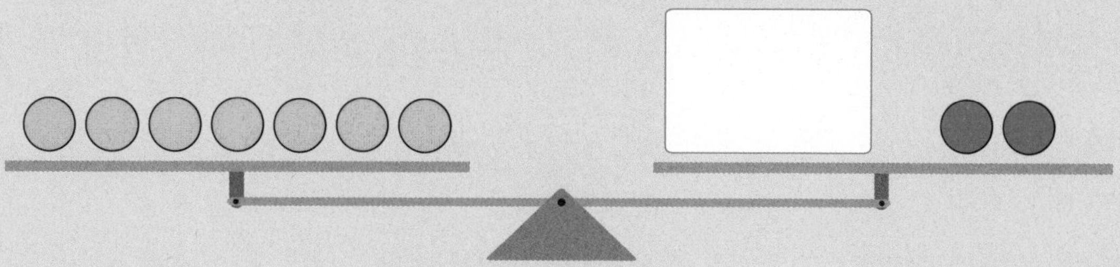

☐ is the same value as ☐ and ☐

b.

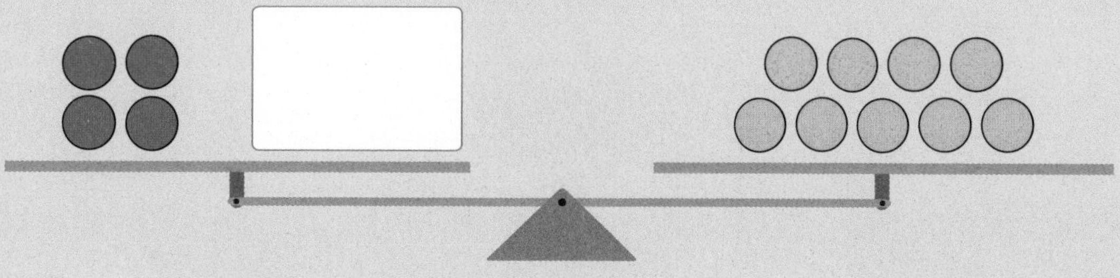

☐ and ☐ balances ☐

c.

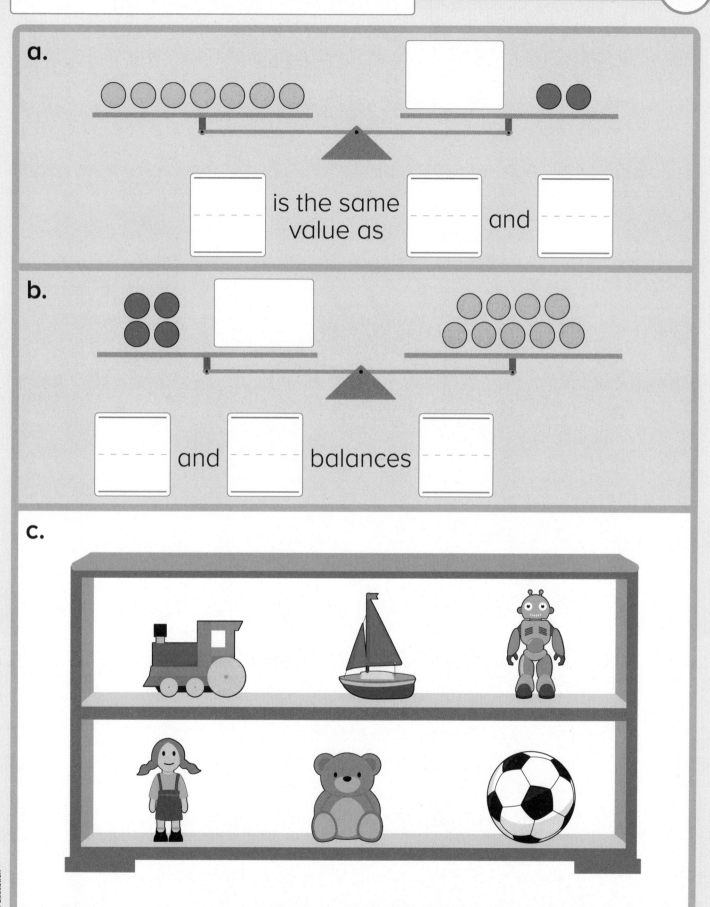

© ORIGO Education

Have the student draw ◯ to make each balance picture true, then complete the matching sentence. Using different colors, they can circle the toy that is just above the ball, the toy that is beside the train, and the toy that is next to the doll.

a.

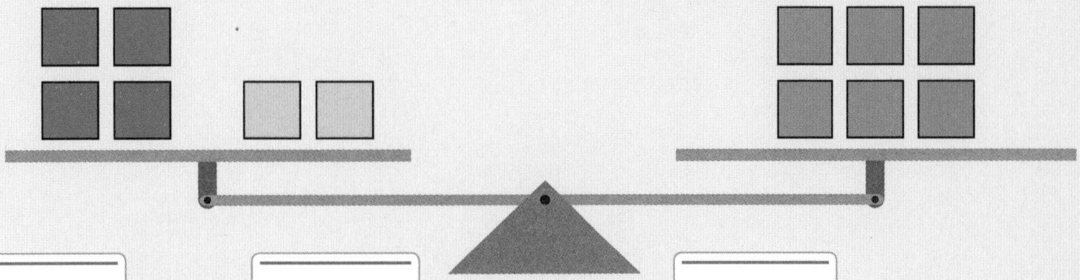

____ and ____ balances ____

b.

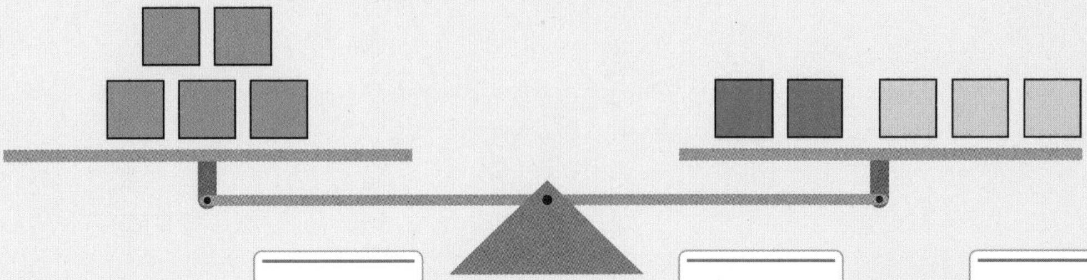

____ balances ____ and ____

c.

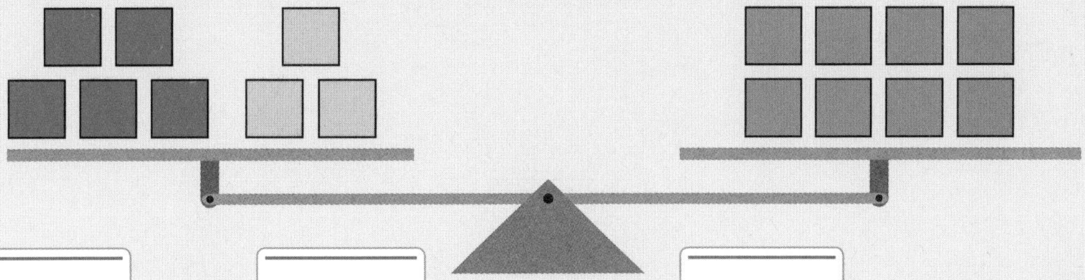

____ and ____ balances ____

d.

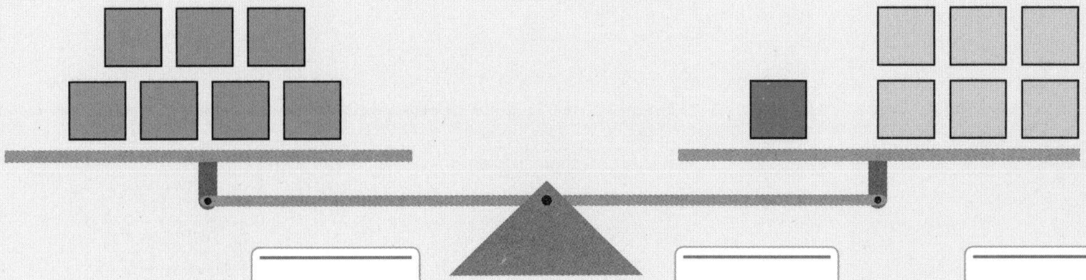

____ balances ____ and ____

© ORIGO Education

Have the student write numbers to match the two groups on one side, then write the total that balances the groups. Repeat for each balance picture.

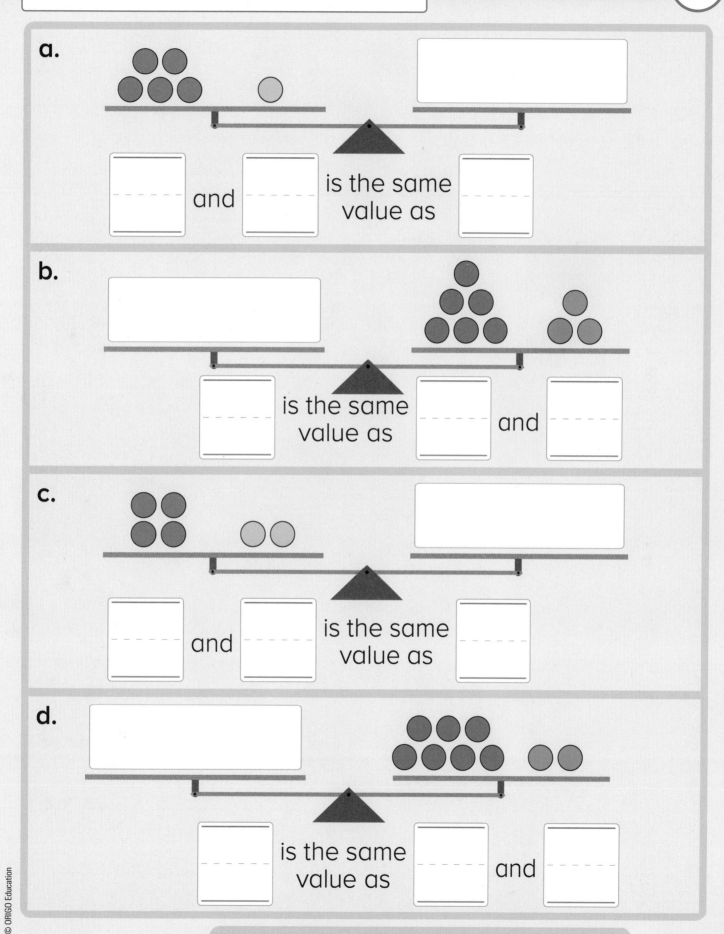

a.

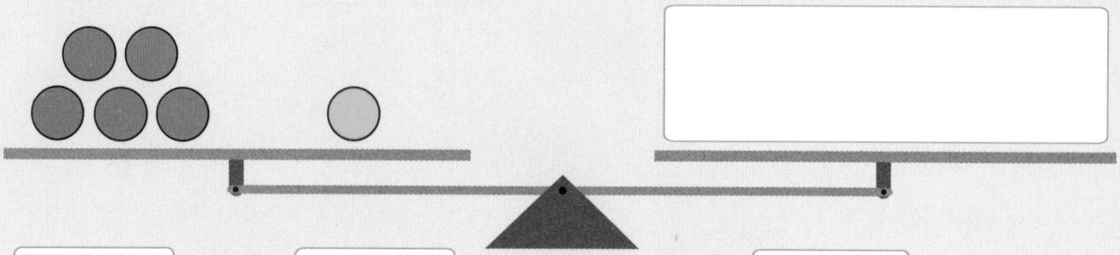

[ ] and [ ] is the same value as [ ]

b.

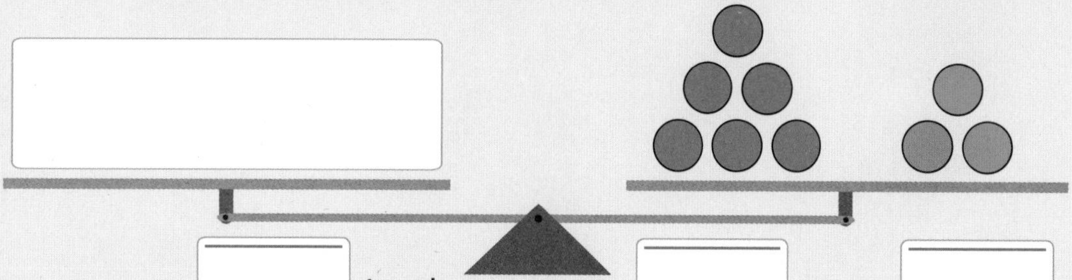

[ ] is the same value as [ ] and [ ]

c.

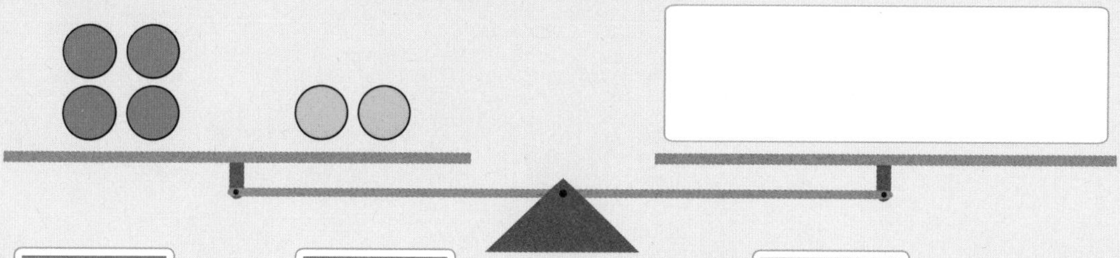

[ ] and [ ] is the same value as [ ]

d.

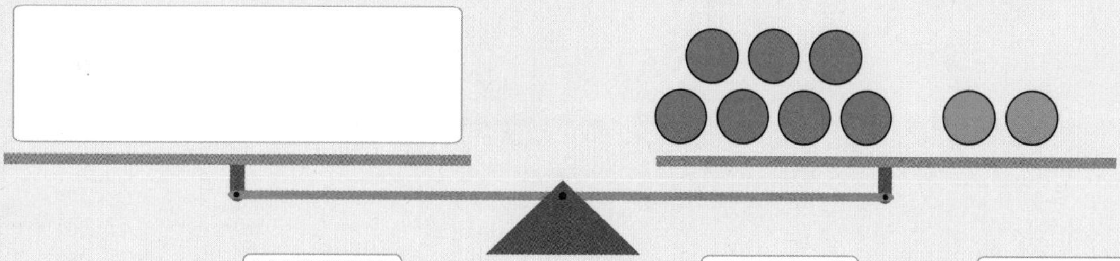

[ ] is the same value as [ ] and [ ]

© ORIGO Education

Have the student draw ◯ to make each balance picture true, then write numbers to complete the matching sentence.

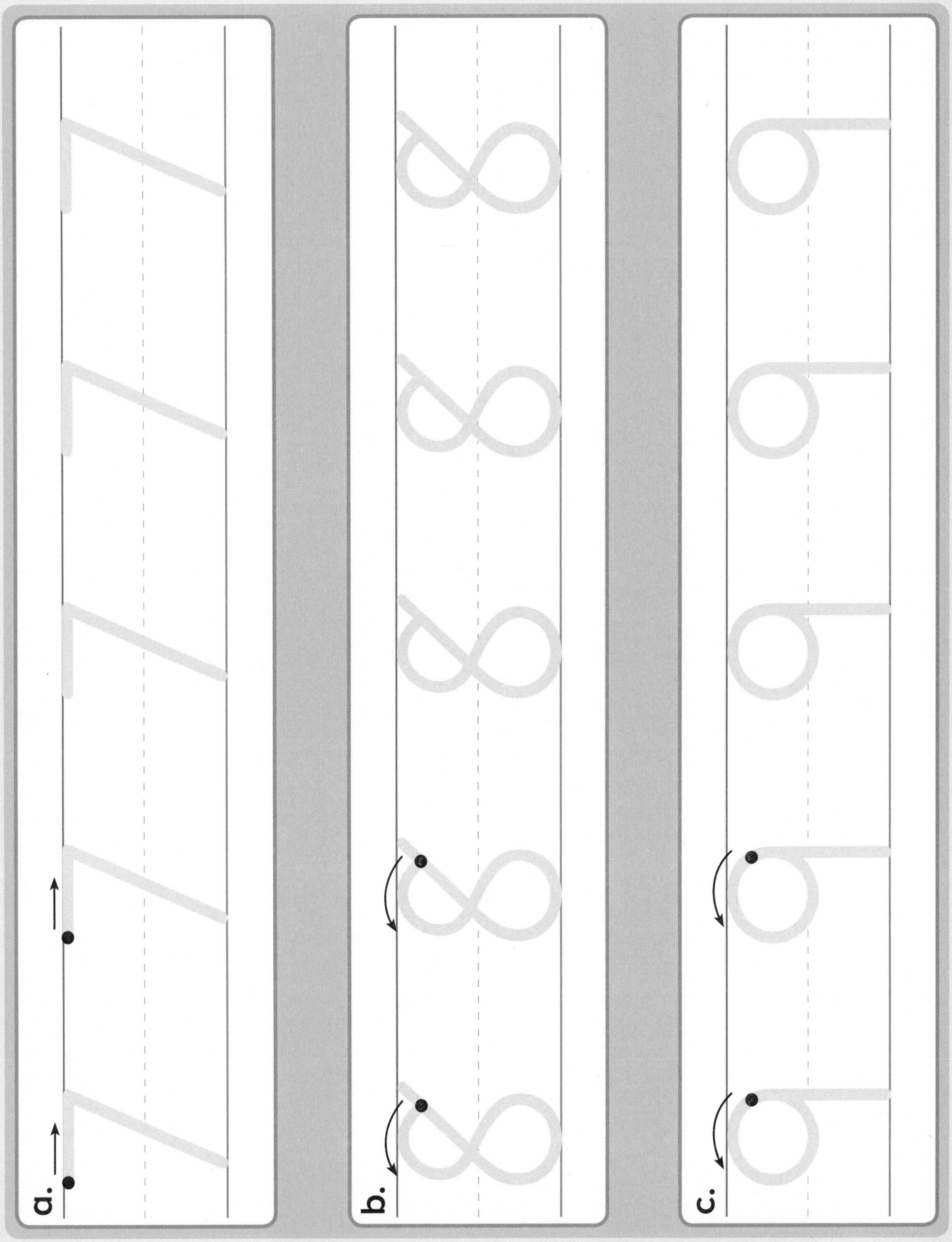

For each of these, have the student say the number aloud, then trace the numeral five times.

© ORIGO Education

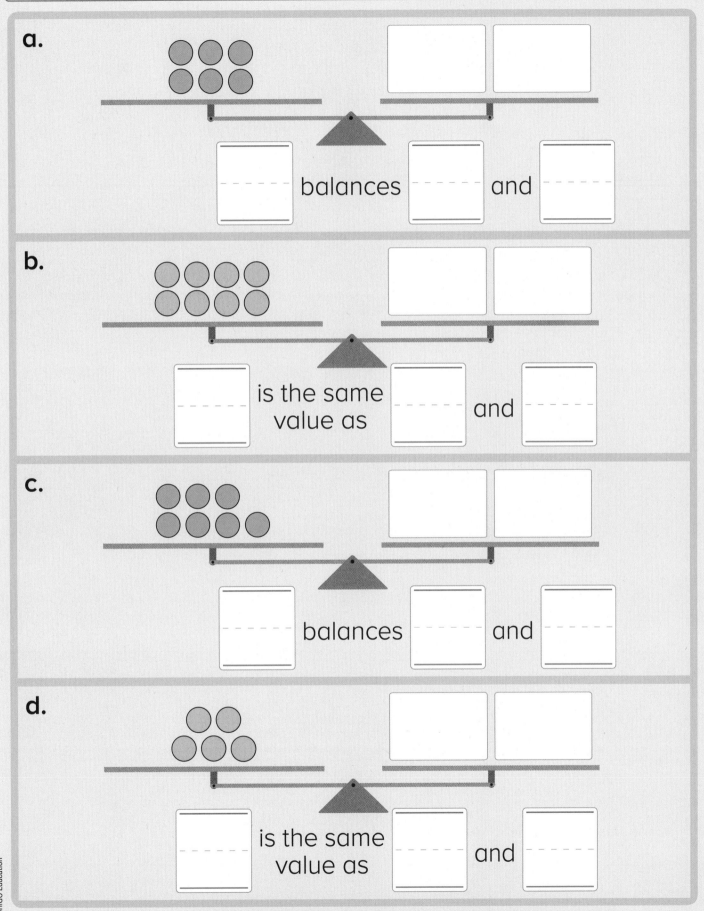

a.

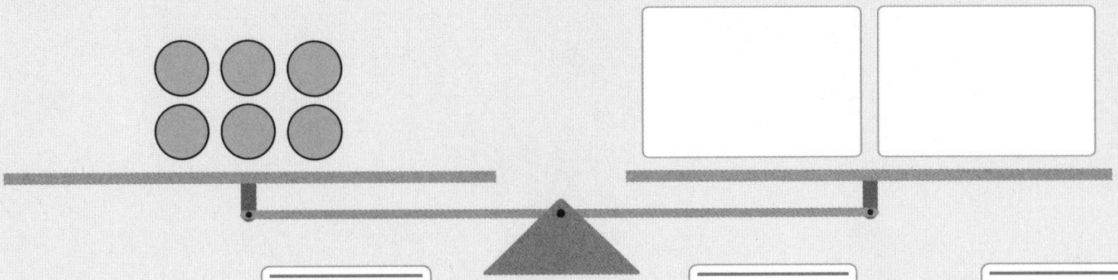

☐ balances ☐ and ☐

b.

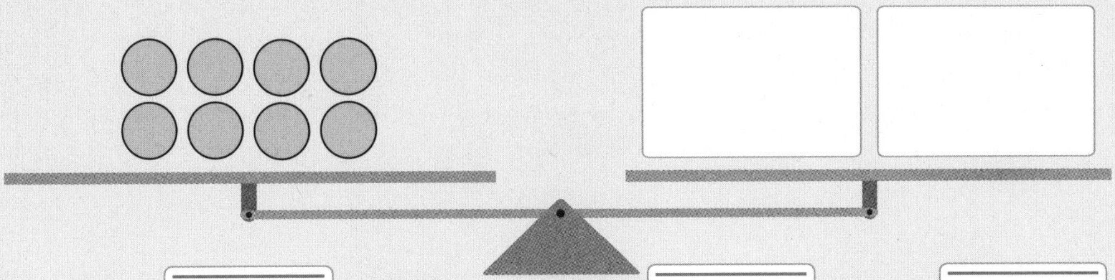

☐ is the same value as ☐ and ☐

c.

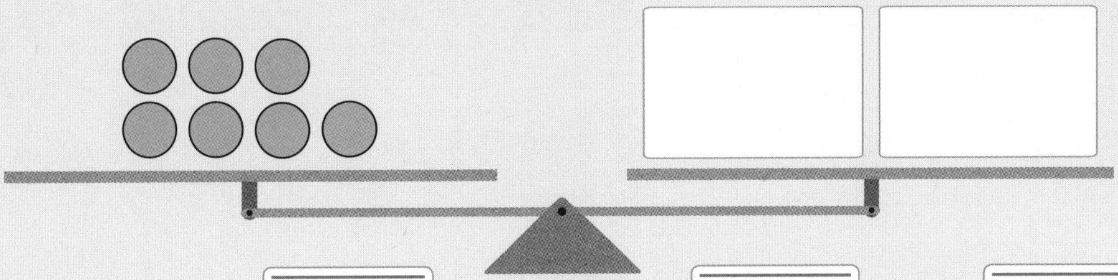

☐ balances ☐ and ☐

d.

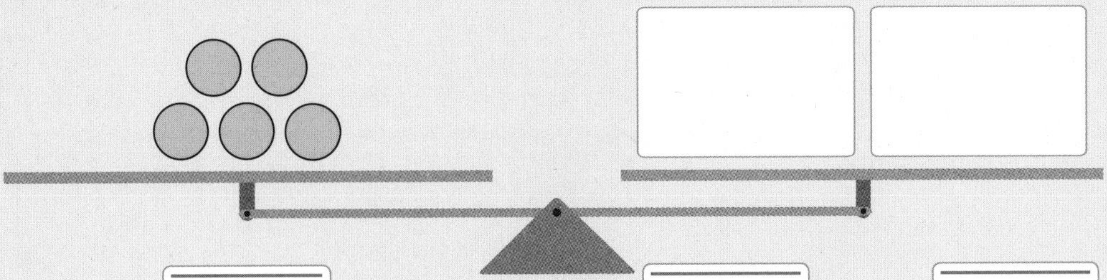

☐ is the same value as ☐ and ☐

Have the student draw ◯ to make each balance picture true, then complete the matching sentence.

© ORIGO Education

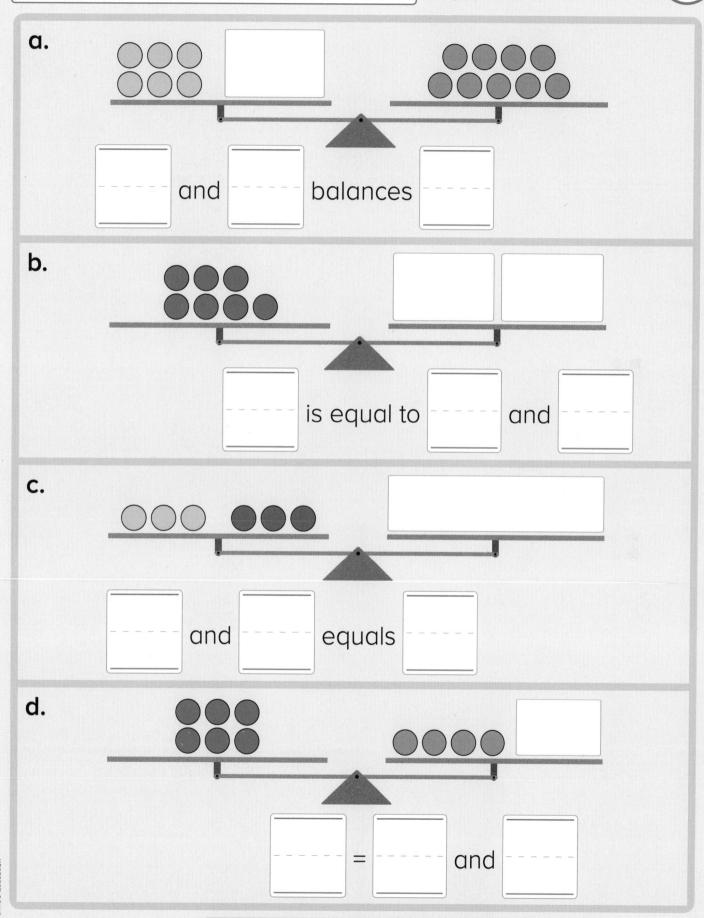

a.

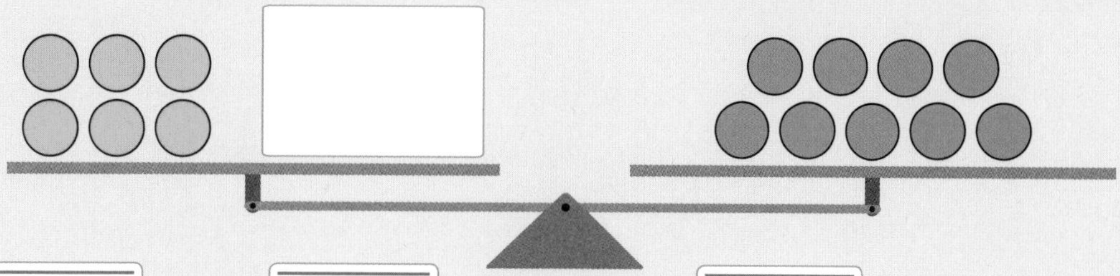

☐ and ☐ balances ☐

b.

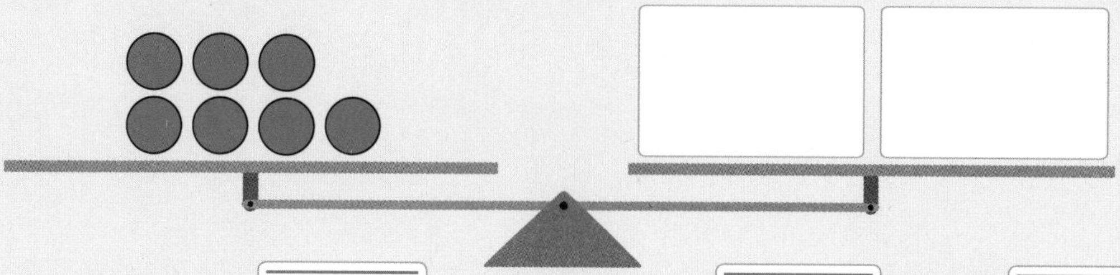

☐ is equal to ☐ and ☐

c.

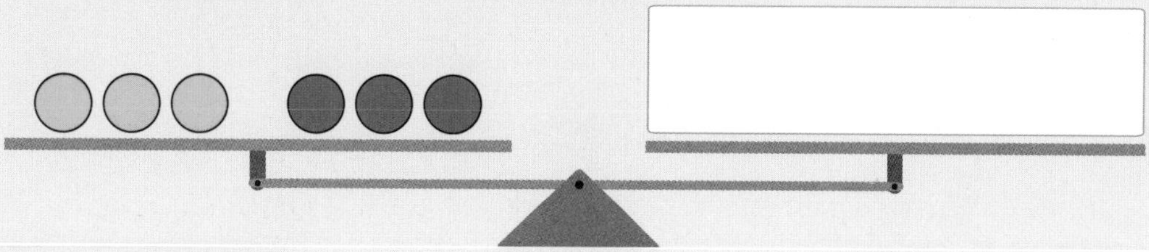

☐ and ☐ equals ☐

d.

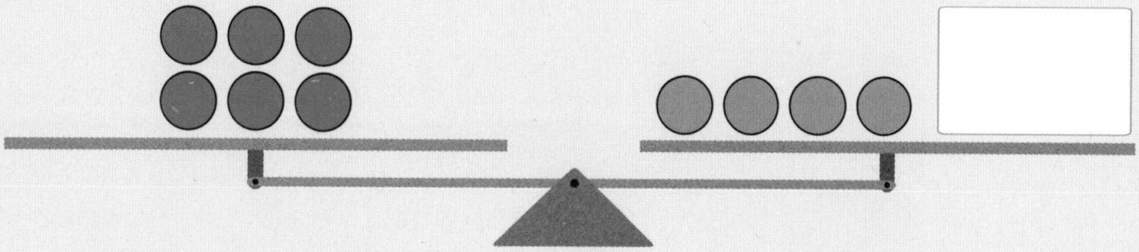

☐ = ☐ and ☐

© ORIGO Education

Have the student draw ◯ to make each balance picture true, then complete the matching sentence or equation.

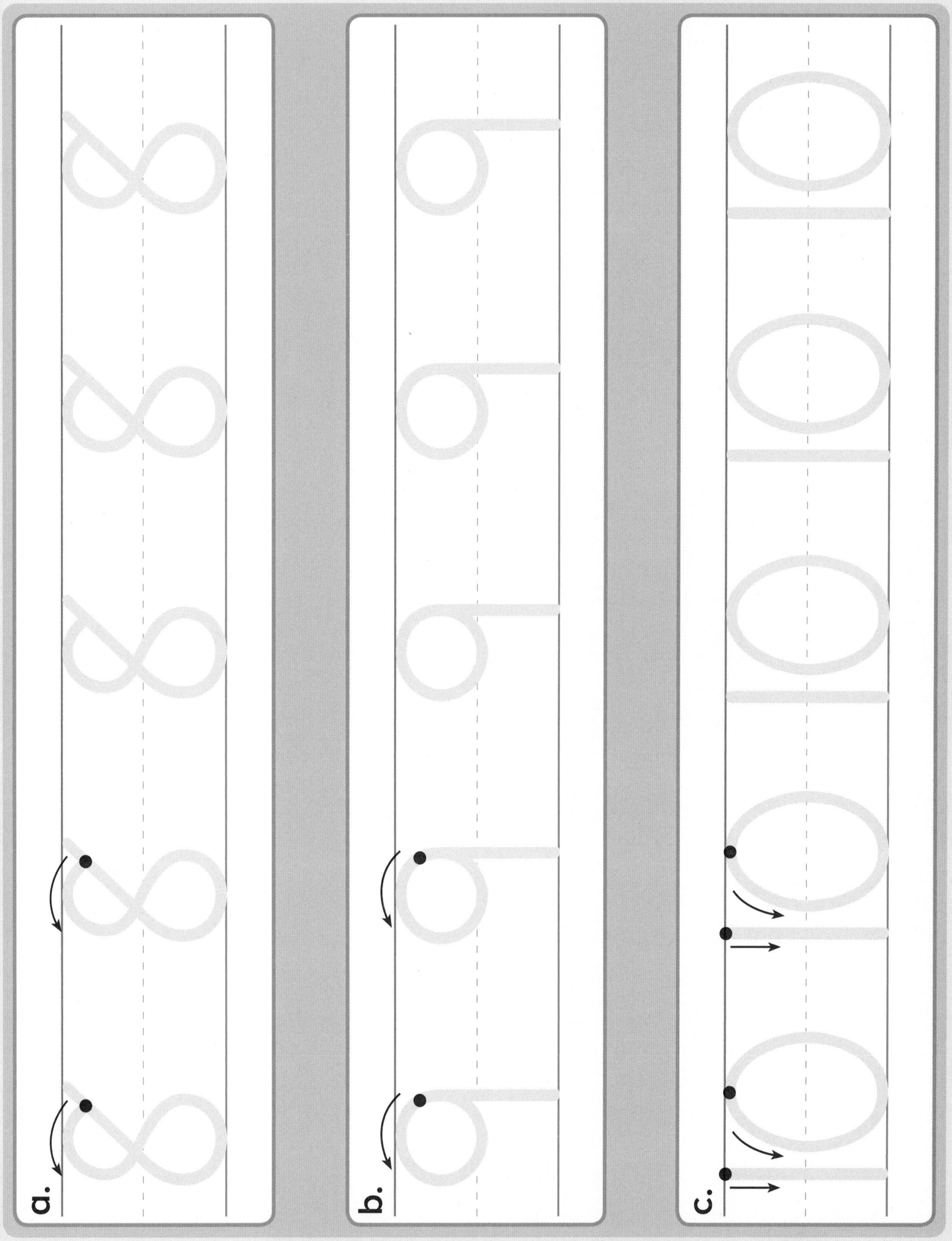

© ORIGO Education

For each of these, have the student say the number aloud, then trace the numeral five times.

a. Draw a  **beside** the tree.

b. Draw a  **on top of** the swing.

c. Draw a 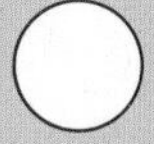 **next to** the dog.

d. Draw a  **above** the clouds.

e. Draw a 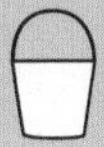 **below** the swing.

© ORIGO Education

Read each instruction aloud. Have the student draw each picture in the correct position.

Have the student color each astronaut's left hand and left foot.

© ORIGO Education

a.	b.	c.	d.
1	2	3	4
1	2	3	4
1	2	3	4
1	2	3	4

For each strip, ask the student to count the dots and say the matching number aloud. Then have the student write the numeral to match the number of dots.

© ORIGO Education

a.

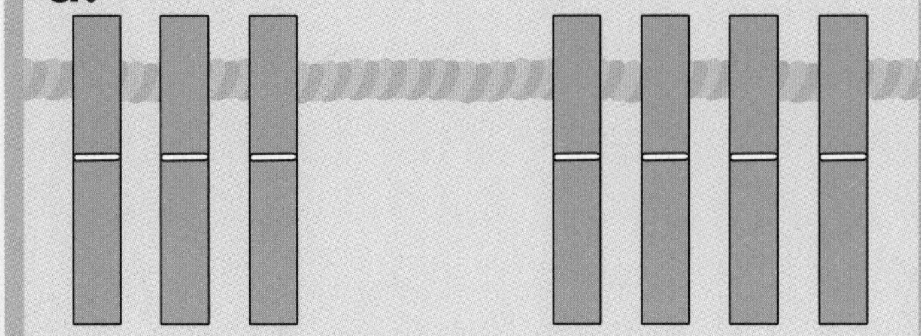

☐ and ☐ is ☐

b.

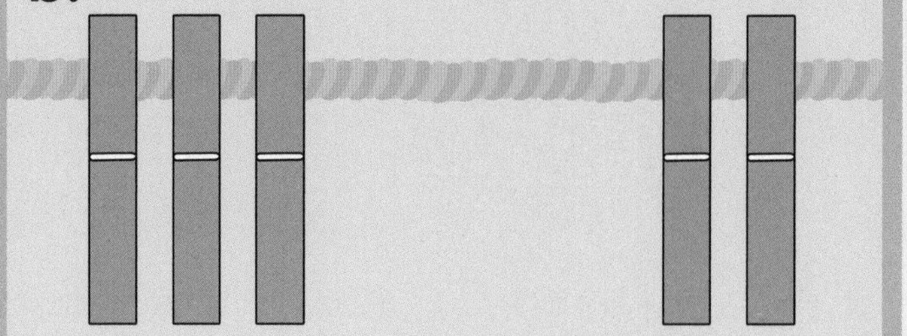

☐ add ☐ is ☐

c.

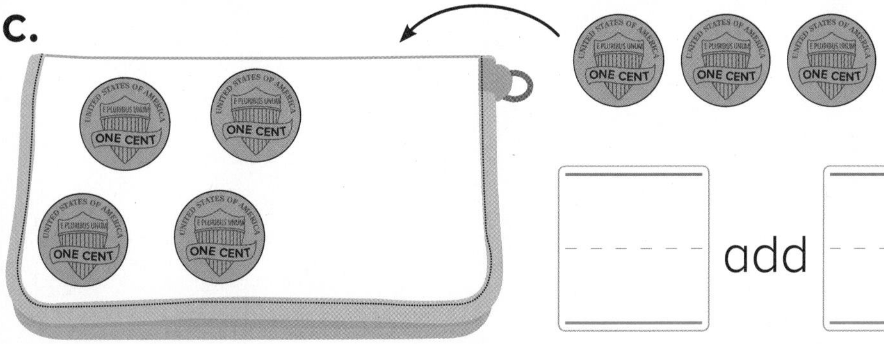

☐ add ☐ is ☐

d.

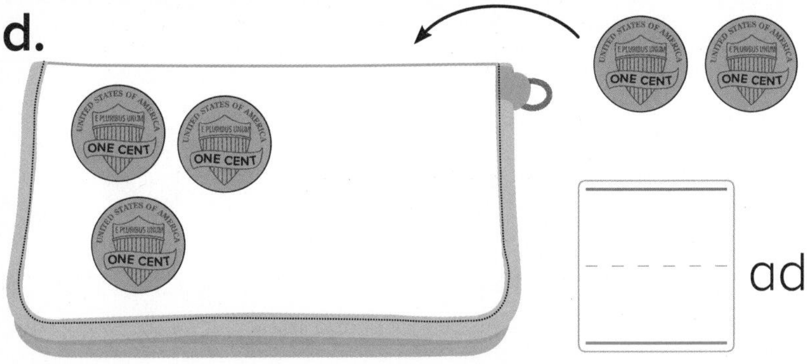

☐ add ☐ equals ☐

e.

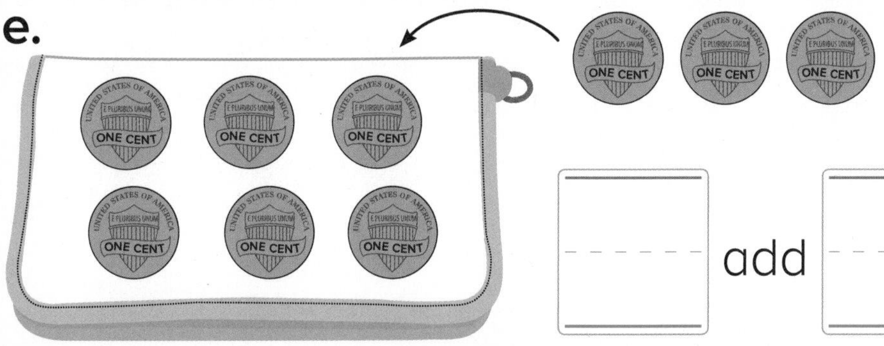

☐ add ☐ = ☐

Have the student write the numbers to match the numbers in the two groups and the total. Then have them write numbers to match the amount in the purse, the amount being added, and the total.

© ORIGO Education

a.

____ and ____ makes ____

b.

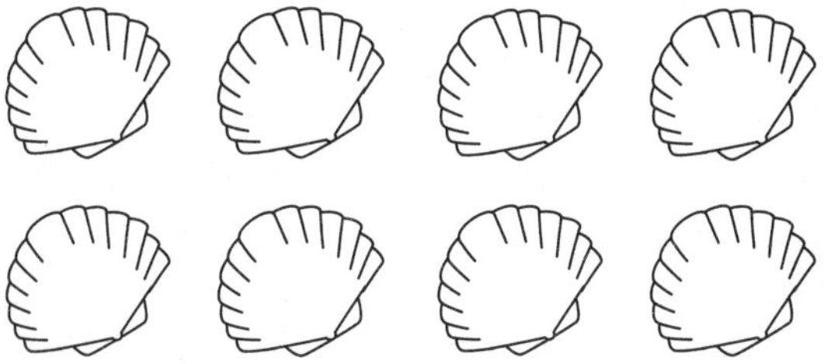

____ and ____ makes ____

c.

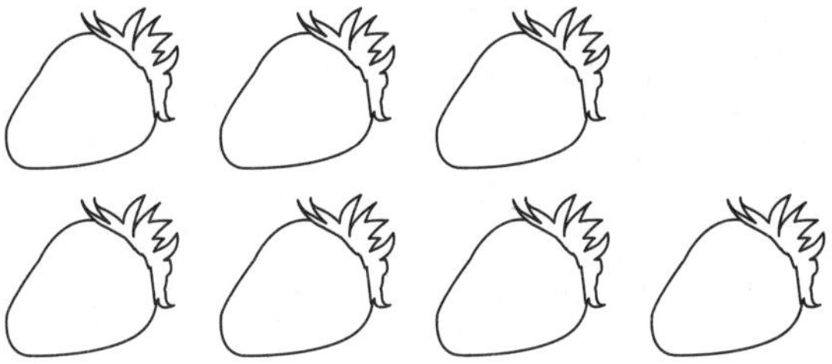

____ plus ____ equals ____

d.

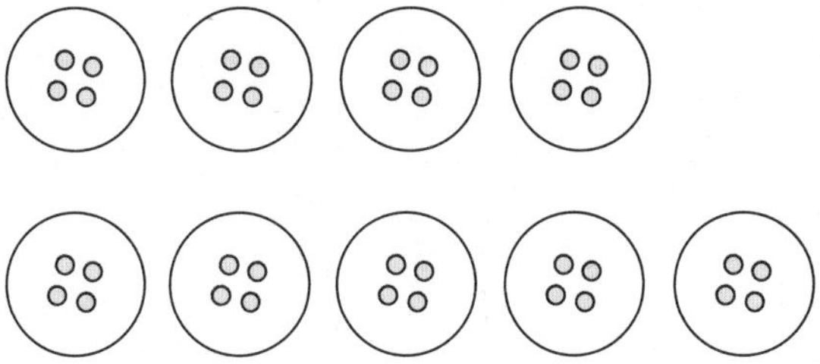

____ add ____ equals ____

© ORIGO Education

For each picture, have the student use two colors to show two different groups, then complete the sentence to match.

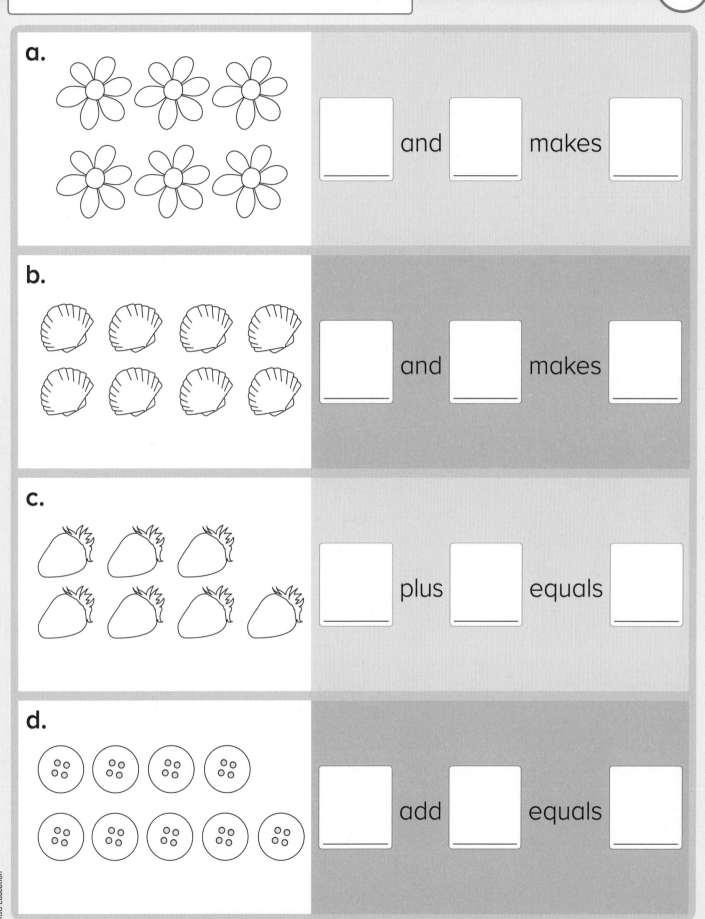

a. Color 3 red.

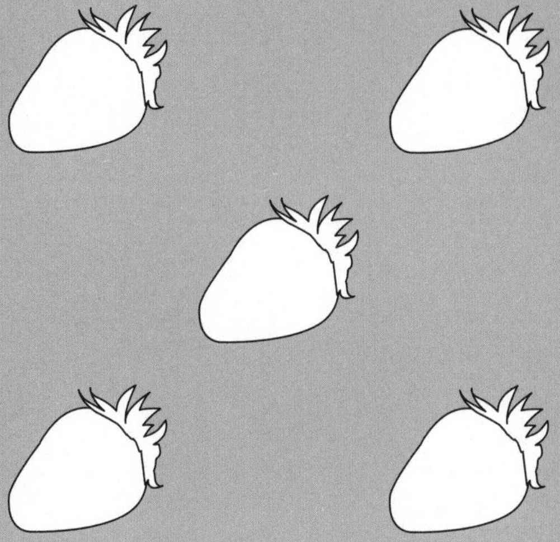

☐ + ☐ = ☐

b. Color 5 red.

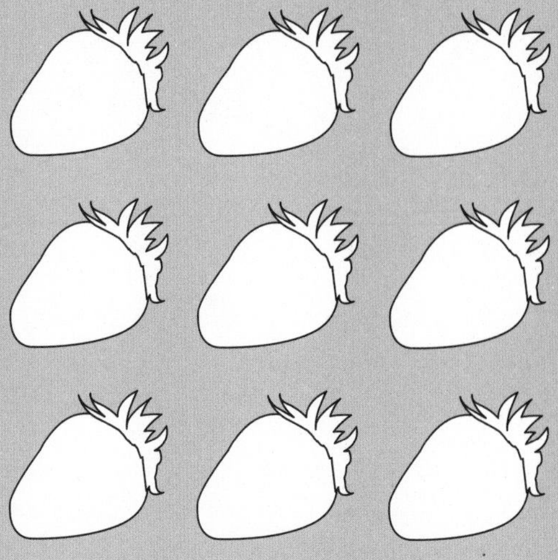

☐ + ☐ = ☐

c. Color 2 red.

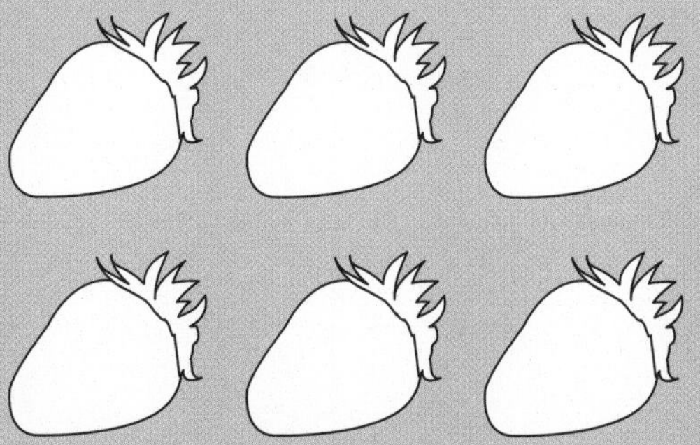

☐ + ☐ = ☐

d. Color 6 red.

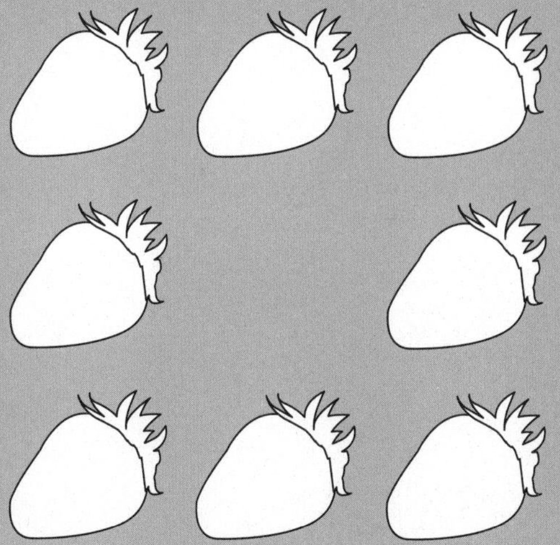

☐ + ☐ = ☐

© ORIGO Education

Have the student color the number of strawberries, then write a matching equation.

a.	b.	c.	d.
2	3	4	5
2	3	4	5
2	3	4	5
2	3	4	5

© ORIGO Education

For each strip, ask the student to count the dots and say the matching number aloud. Then have the student write the numeral to match the number of dots.

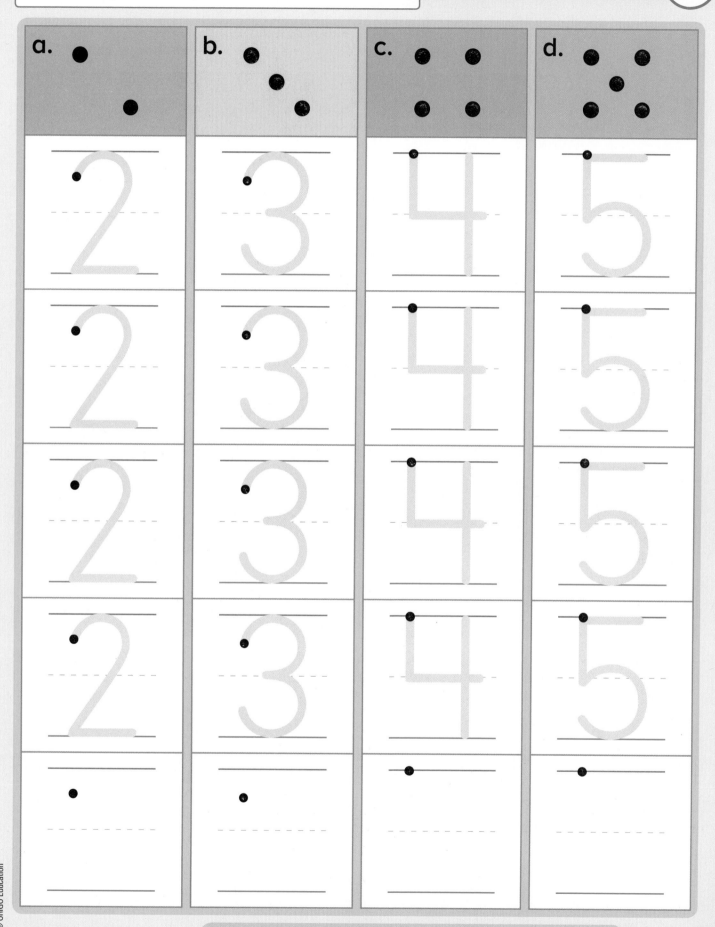

a.

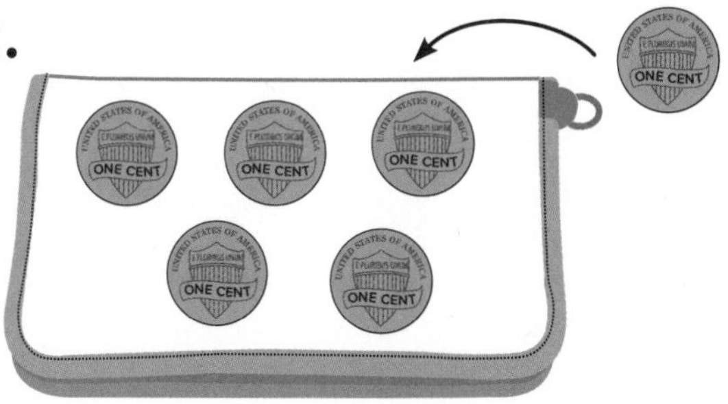

____ add ____ makes ____

b.

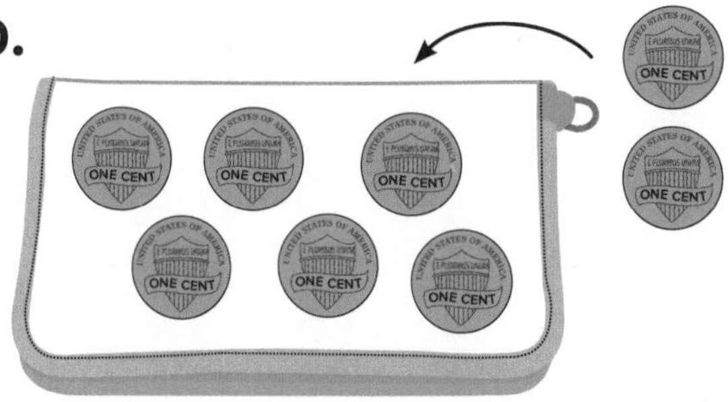

____ add ____ is ____

c.

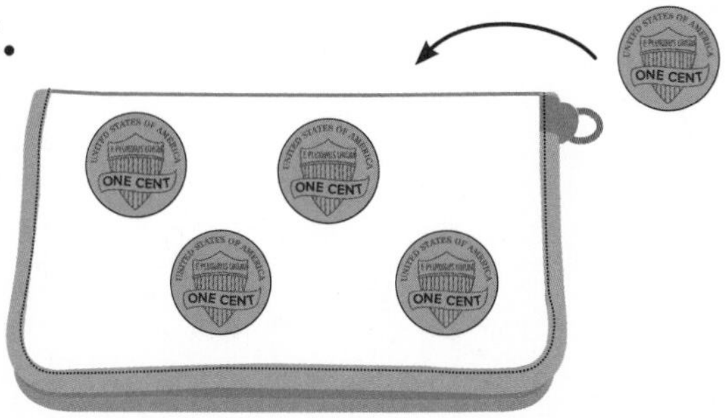

____ add ____ equals ____

d.

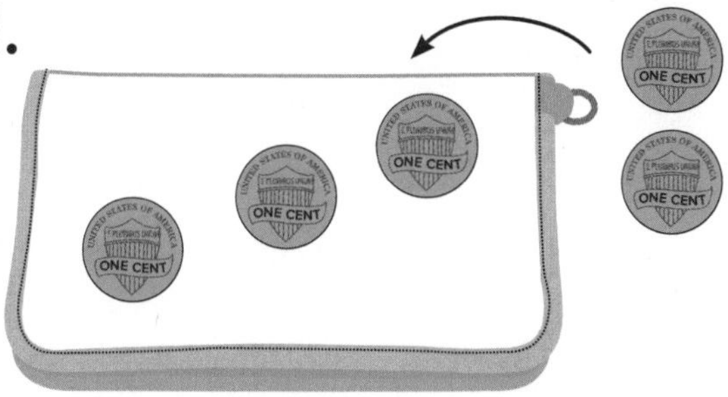

____ add ____ = ____

e.

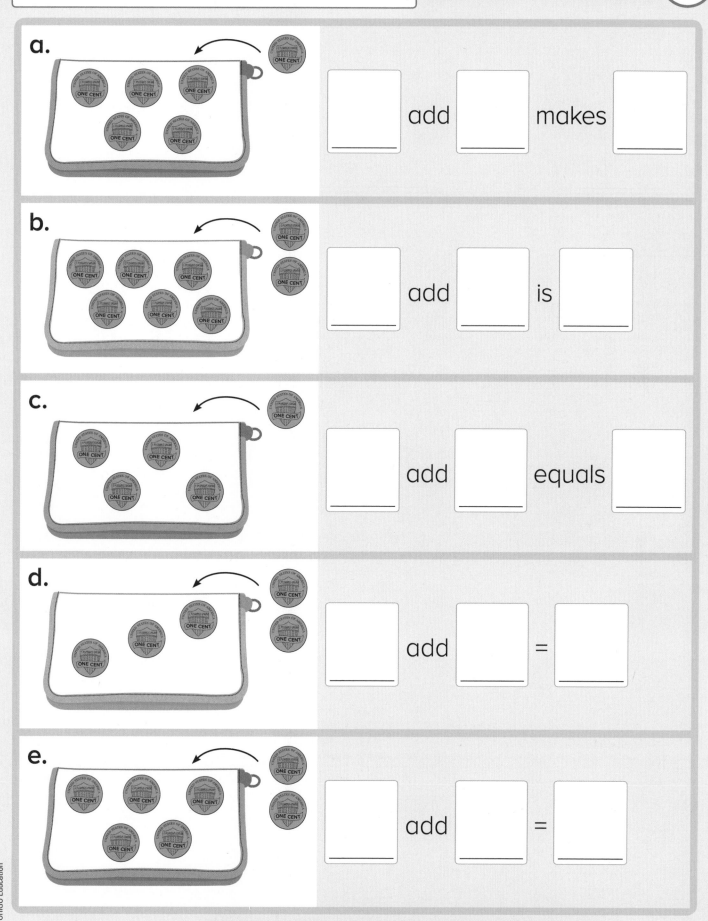

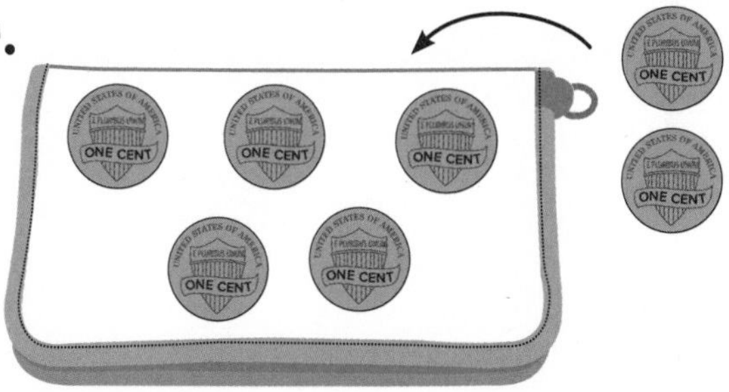

____ add ____ = ____

© ORIGO Education

Have the student write the amount in the purse, the amount being added, and the total.

a.

$\square + \square = \square$

b.

$\square + \square = \square$

c.

$\square + \square = \square$

d.

$\square + \square = \square$

e.

$\square + \square = \square$

Have the student write an equation to match each picture.

© ORIGO Education

a.	b.	c.	d.
3	4	5	6
3	4	5	6
3	4	5	6
3	4	5	6

© ORIGO Education

For each strip, ask the student to count the dots and say the matching number aloud. Then have the student write the numeral to match the number of dots.

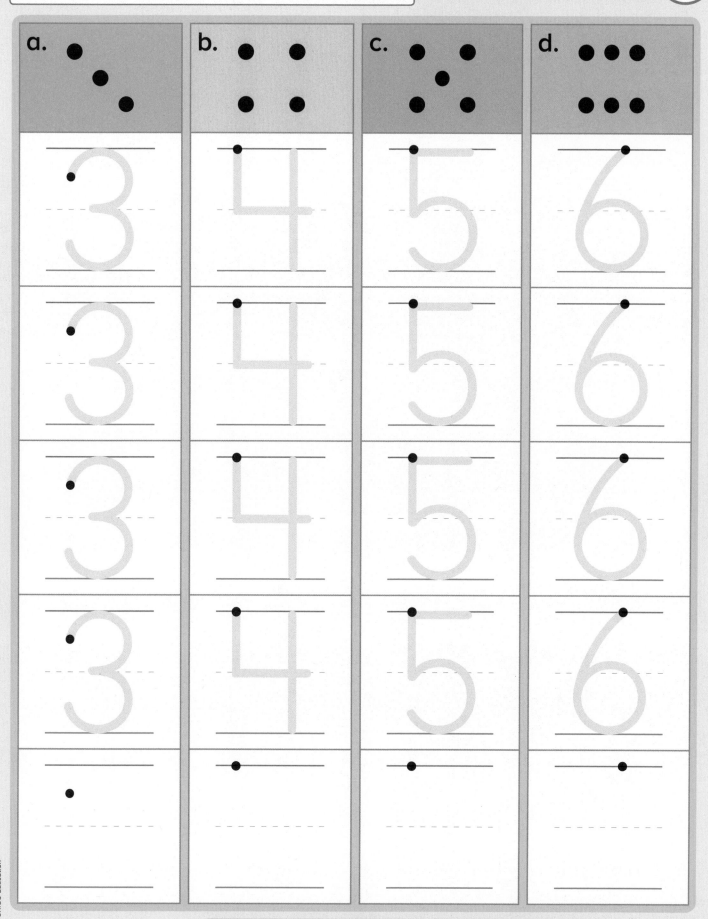

a.

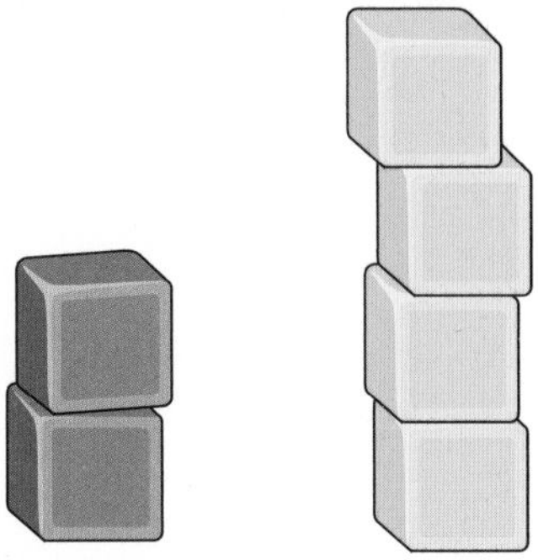

___ + ___ = ___

b.

___ + ___ = ___

c.

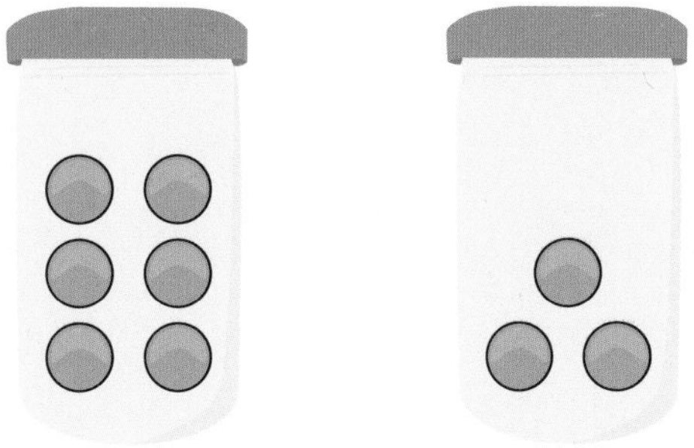

___ + ___ = ___

d.

___ + ___ = ___

e.

___ + ___ = ___

© ORIGO Education

Have the student write an equation to match each picture.

Start

5 + 0 = ___

2 + 3 = ___

0 + 2 = ___

3 + 2 = ___

4 + 1 = ___

2 + 1 = ___

1 + 1 = ___

0 + 4 = ___

1 + 2 = ___

1 + 3 = ___

2 + 2 = ___

3 + 0 = ___

3 + 1 = ___

1 + 4 = ___

0 + 1 = ___

Finish

© ORIGO Education

Have the student write the totals.

a.	b.	c.	d.
● ● ● ●	● ● ● ● ●	● ● ● ● ● ●	● ● ● ● ● ● ●
4	5	6	7
4	5	6	7
4	5	6	7
4	5	6	7

For each strip, ask the student to count the dots and say the matching number aloud. Then have the student write the numeral to match the number of dots.

© ORIGO Education

a.

16

sixteen

b.

19

nineteen

c.

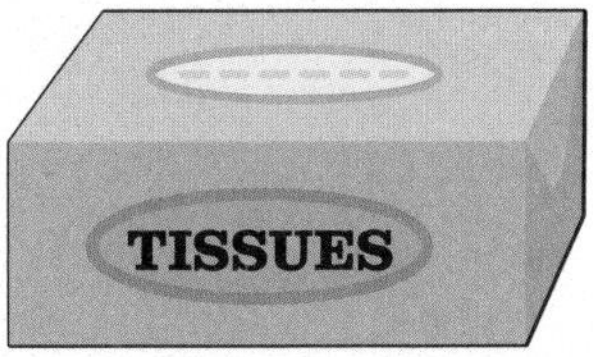

© ORIGO Education

Ask the student to read the number aloud, draw the matching number of ◯ and trace over the number name. Then have the student circle the objects that can roll.

a. 17 seventeen

b. 16 sixteen

c. 14 fourteen

© ORIGO Education

Have the student place 17 pennies (or any small item) in the empty space, then trace over the matching number name. Ask the student to remove all the pennies, then repeat for 16 and 14.

a. 15 fifteen

b. 19 nineteen

c. 18 eighteen

© ORIGO Education

Have the student place 15 pennies (or any small item) in the empty space, then trace over the matching number name. Ask the student to remove all the pennies, then repeat for 19 and 18.

a. 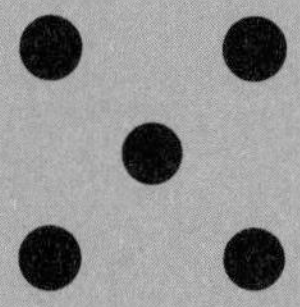

5 5 5 5

b. 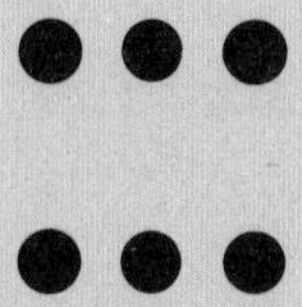

6 6 6 6

c. 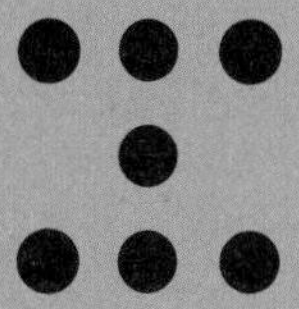

7 7 7 7

d. 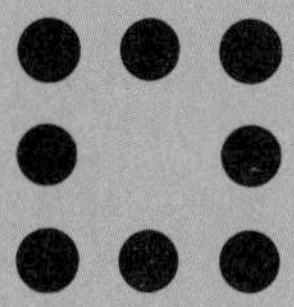

8 8 8 8

For each strip, ask the student to count the dots and say the matching number aloud. Then have the student write the numeral to match the number of dots.

© ORIGO Education

a. 11 eleven

b. 13 thirteen

c. 20 twenty

d. 12 twelve

© ORIGO Education

Have the student place 11 pennies (or any small item) in the empty space, then trace over the matching number name. Ask the student to remove all the pennies, then repeat for 13, 20, and 12.

a.

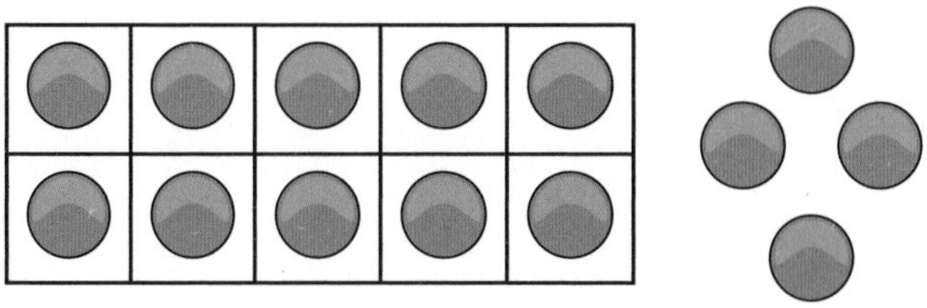

_____ ten and _____ ones

b.

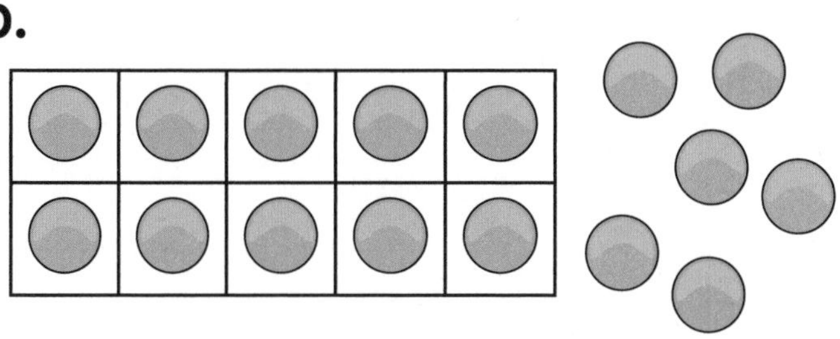

_____ ten and _____ ones

c.

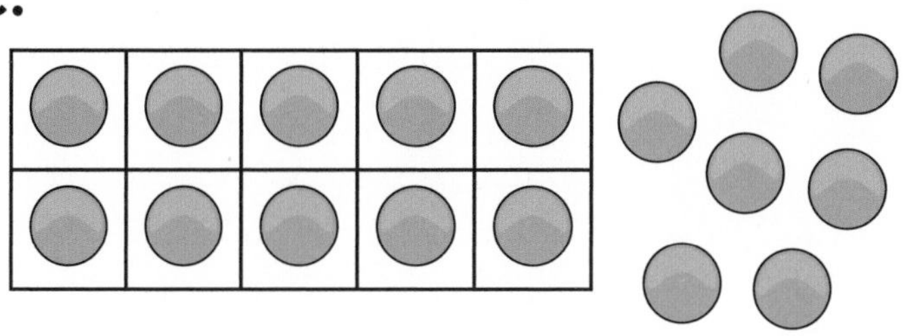

_____ ten and _____ ones

d.

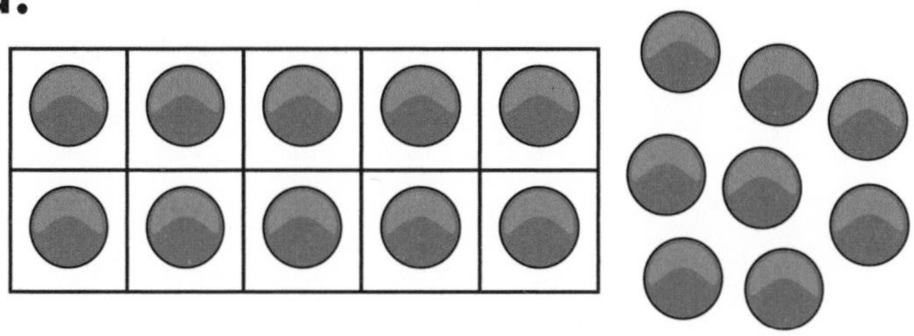

_____ ten and _____ ones

e.

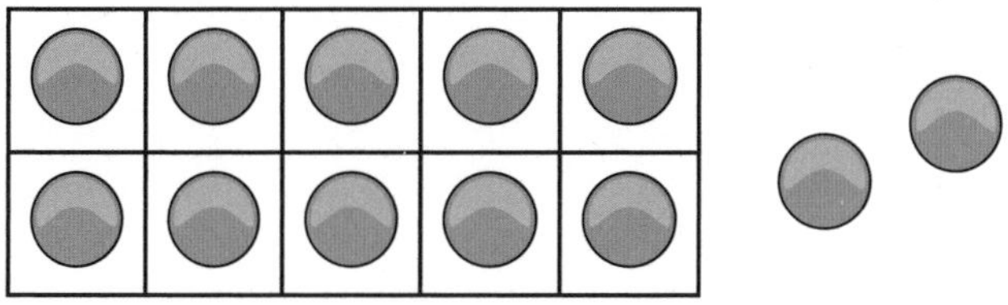

_____ ten and _____ ones

© ORIGO Education

Have the student write the number of tens and ones.

a.	b.	c.	d.
6	7	8	9
6	7	8	9
6	7	8	9
6	7	8	9

For each strip, ask the student to count the dots and say the matching number aloud. Then have the student write the numeral to match the number of dots.

© ORIGO Education

a. all flat surfaces

b. all curved surfaces

c. flat and curved surfaces

© ORIGO Education

Have the student draw or cut out one or two pictures of objects from catalogs or magazines and paste them in a matching space above.

a.

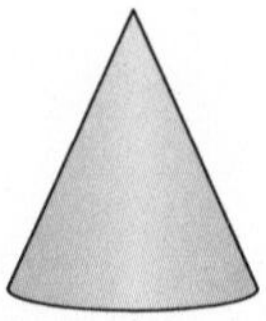

b.

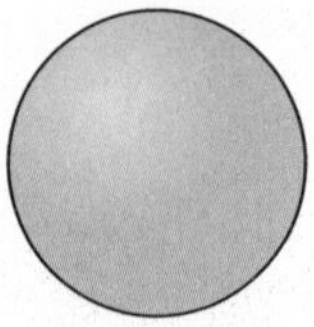

c.

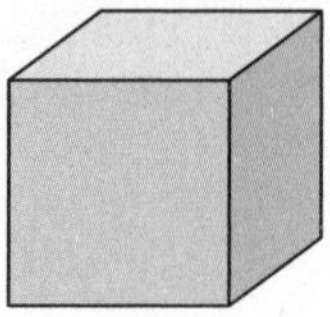

d.

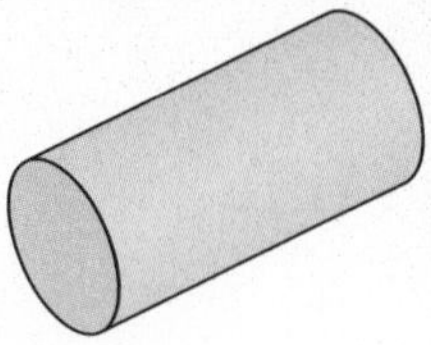

sphere	cube	cone	cylinder

© ORIGO Education

Have the student cut out and paste each label beside a matching picture. Then cut out one picture of a matching object from a catalog or magazine and paste it in each remaining space.

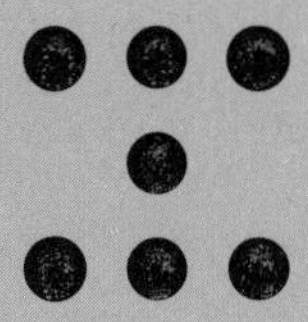

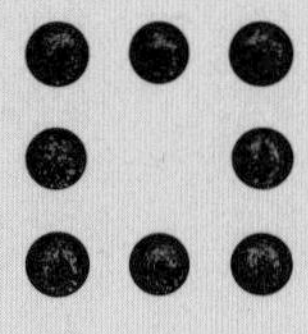

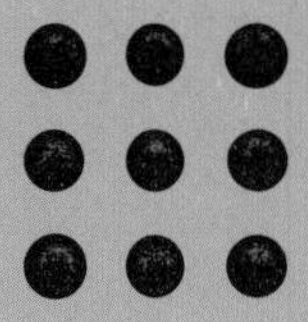

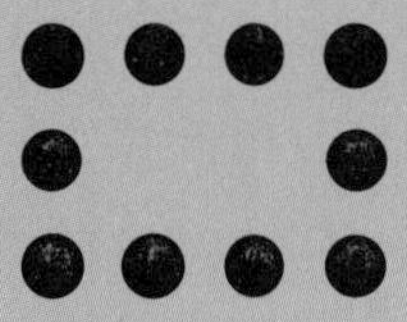

a.	b.	c.	d.
7	8	9	10
7	8	9	10
7	8	9	10
7	8	9	10

For each strip, ask the student to count the dots and say the matching number aloud. Then have the student write the numeral to match the number of dots.

151

© ORIGO Education

a.

7 cross out 4 is ___

b.

___ less 5 = ___

c.

___ take away 2 = ___

d.

___ take away 3 is ___

e.

___ subtract 2 = ___

f.

___ – 4 = ___

© ORIGO Education

For the first three examples, have the student cross out objects to match the number shown. Then ask them to complete a matching sentence or equation for every picture.

a.

6 coins

____ cross out 4 is ____

b.

9 eggs

____ less 3 is ____

c.

5 flowers

____ less 1 is ____

d.

7 blocks

____ subtract 5 is ____

For each of these, have the student cross out the number shown, then complete the sentence to match the picture.

© ORIGO Education

a.

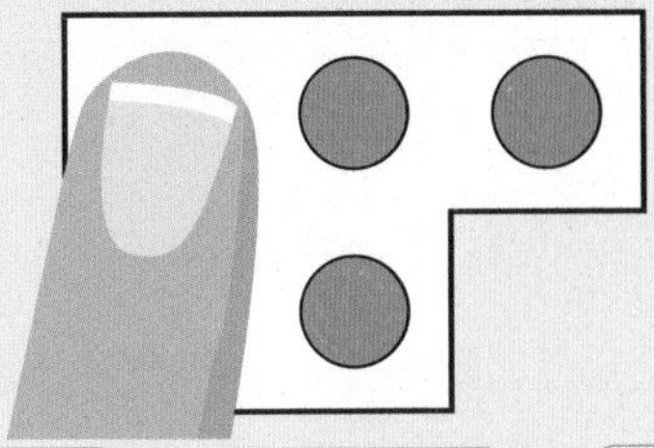

5 − 2 = ____

b.

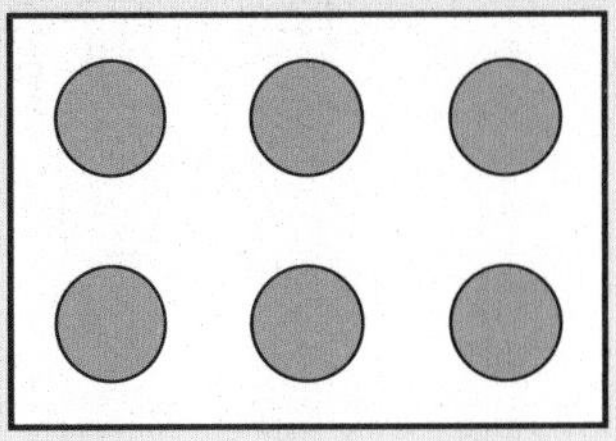

____ − 1 = ____

c.

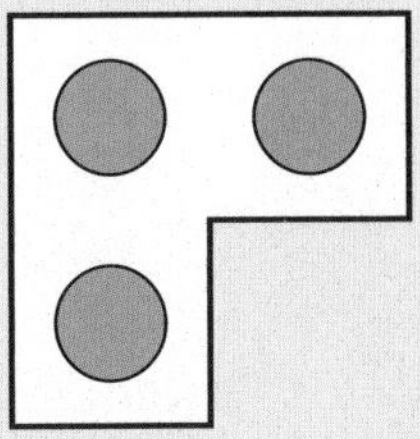

____ − 1 = ____

d.

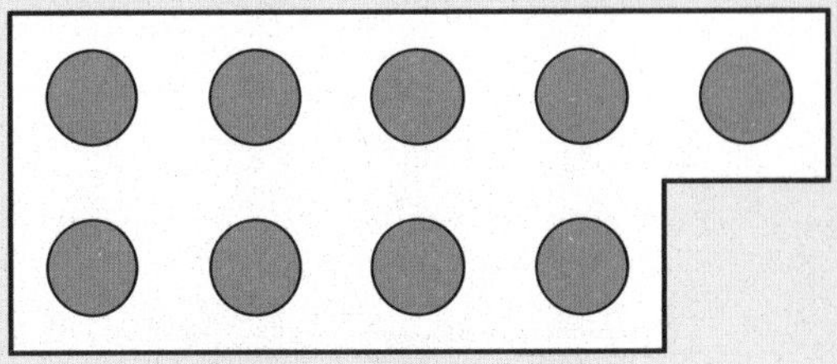

____ − 2 = ____

e.

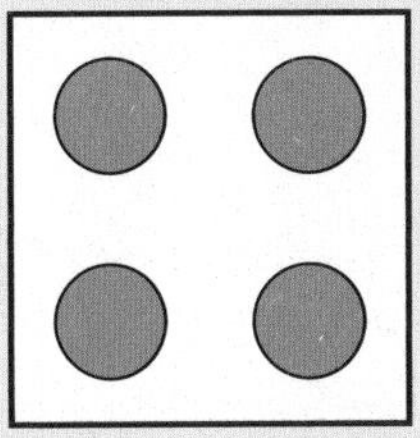

____ − 2 = ____

f.

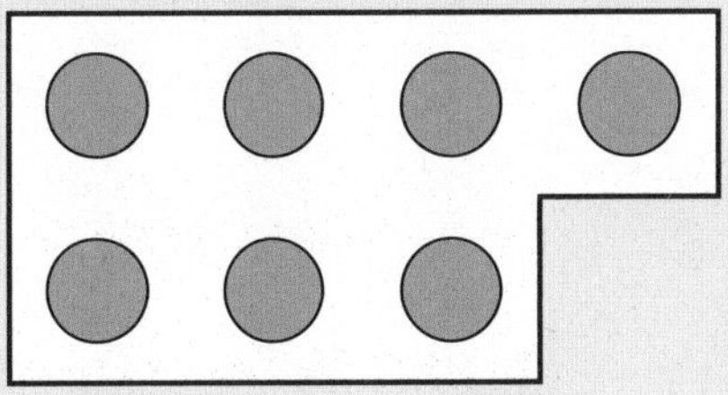

____ − 1 = ____

g.

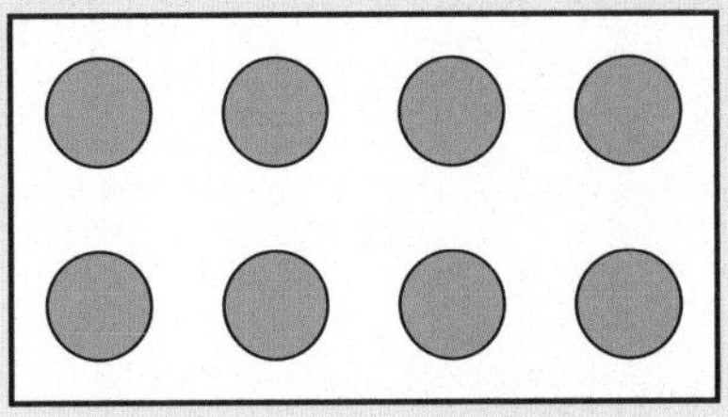

____ − 1 = ____

h.

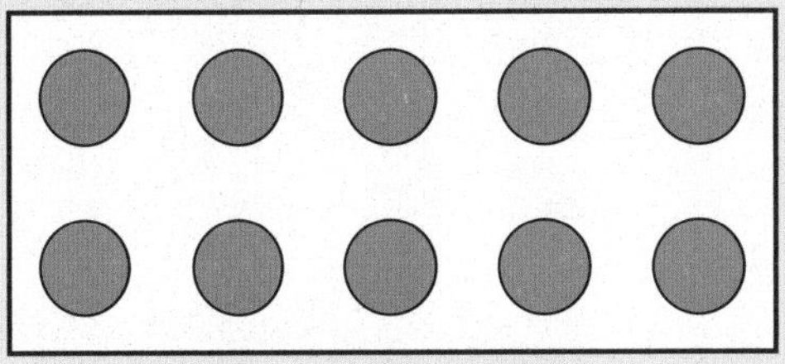

____ − 2 = ____

For each of these, have the student write the total number of dots, then cover 1 or 2 dots (as shown in a.), and write the number of dots that are left.

© ORIGO Education

a. 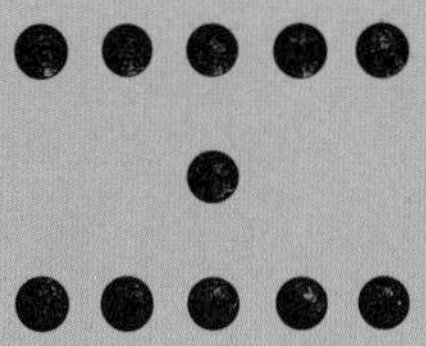

11

11

11

11

b. 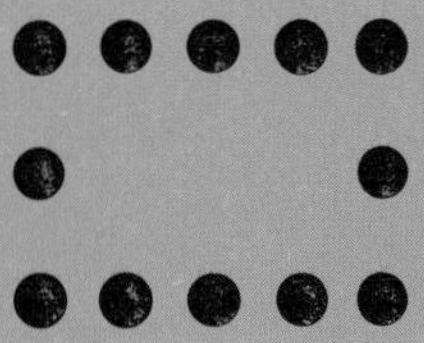

12

12

12

12

c. 

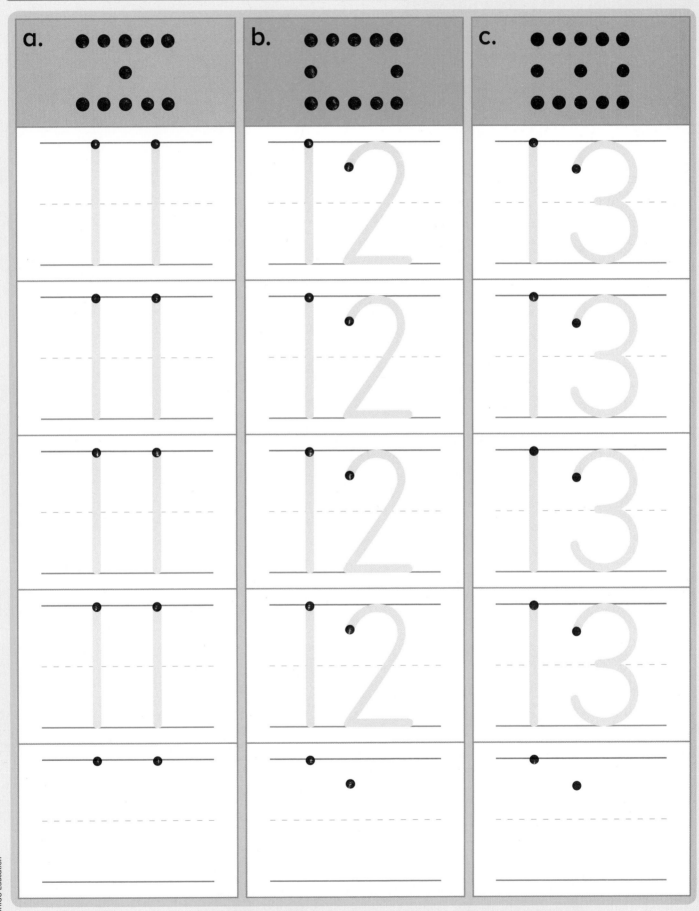

13

13

13

13

For each strip, ask the student to count the dots and say the matching number aloud. Then have the student write the numeral to match the number of dots.

© ORIGO Education

a.

6 take away 2 is ____

b.

____ less ____ is ____

c.

____ less ____ is ____

d.

____ less ____ is ____

e.

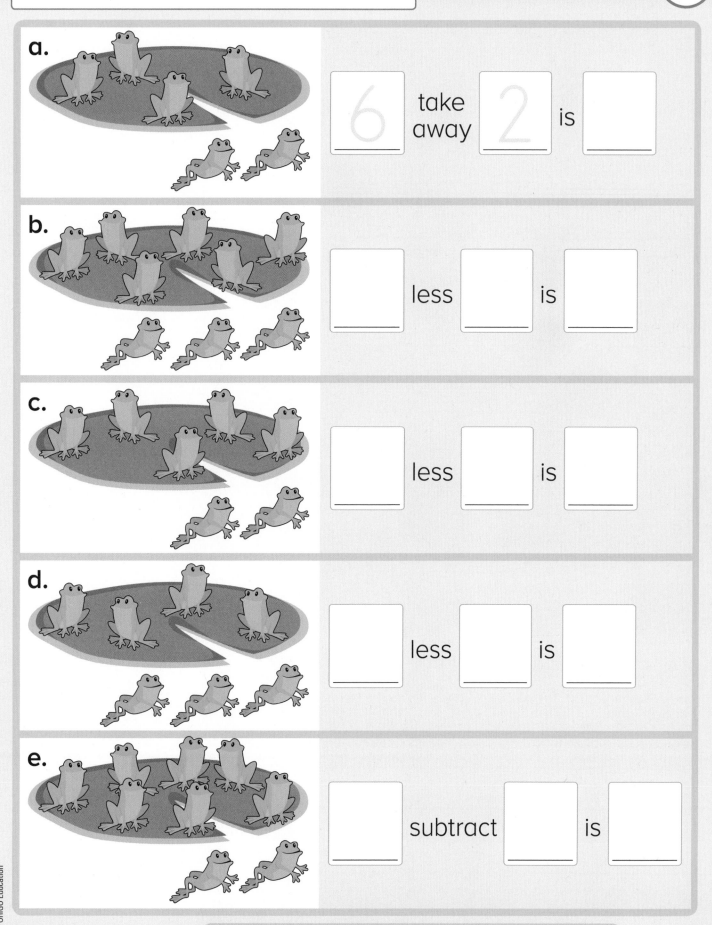

____ subtract ____ is ____

© ORIGO Education

Have the student write the total number of frogs and the number jumping away, then complete the sentence to match the picture.

a.

6 – 2 = ____

b.

____ – ____ = ____

c.

____ – ____ = ____

d.

____ – ____ = ____

e.

____ – ____ = ____

f.

____ – ____ = ____

For each of these, have the student write an equation to match the picture.

© ORIGO Education

a.	b.	c.
	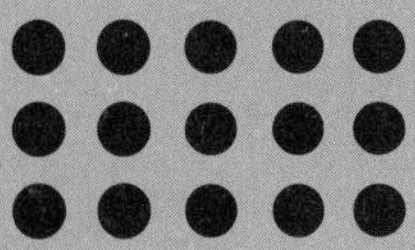	
14	15	16
14	15	16
14	15	16
14	15	16

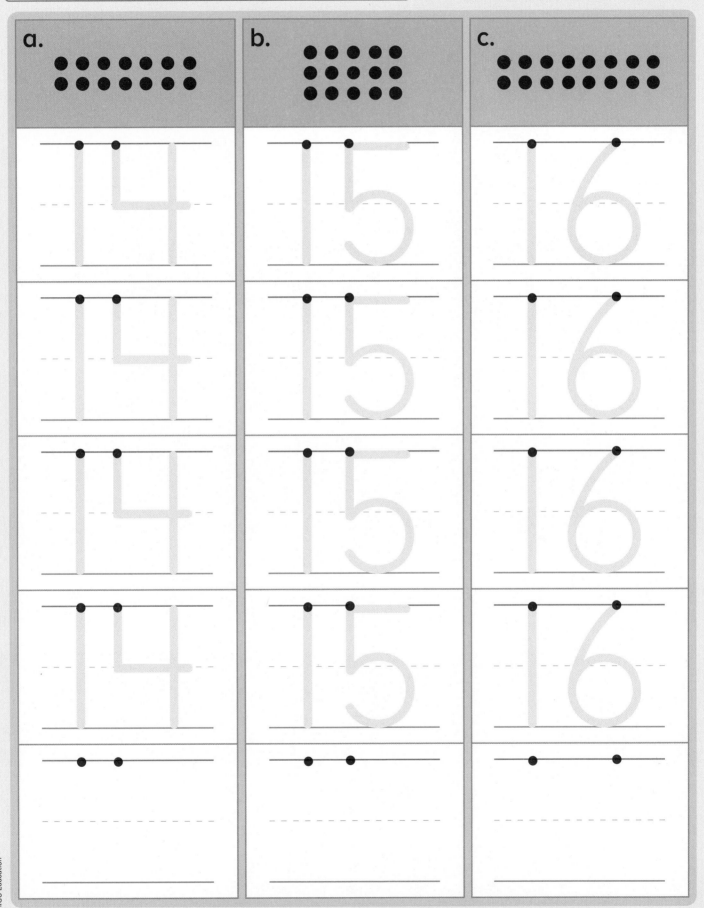

For each strip, ask the student to count the dots and say the matching number aloud. Then have the student write the numeral to match the number of dots.

© ORIGO Education

a.

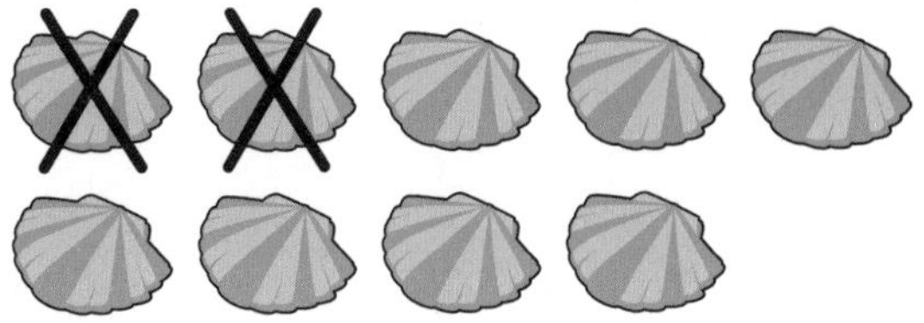

☐ – ☐ = ☐

b.

☐ – ☐ = ☐

c.

☐ – ☐ = ☐

d.

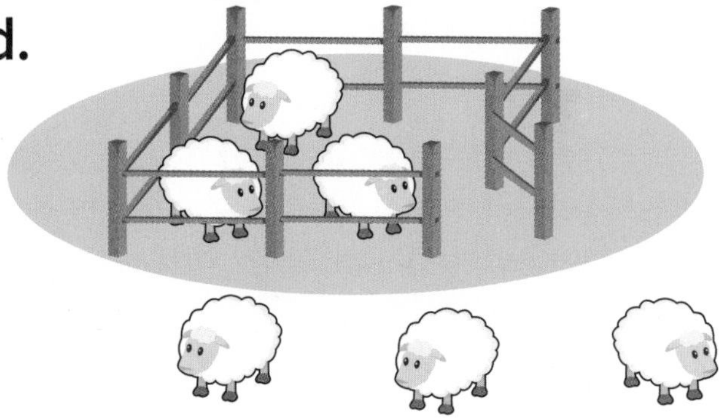

☐ – ☐ = ☐

e.

☐ – ☐ = ☐

f.

☐ – ☐ = ☐

© ORIGO Education

For each of these, have the student write an equation to match the picture.

Start

4 - 2 = ___

3 - 3 = ___

1 - 1 = ___

4 - 3 = ___

2 - 2 = ___

5 - 0 = ___

5 - 4 = ___

4 - 1 = ___

5 - 2 = ___

2 - 1 = ___

4 - 4 = ___

3 - 1 = ___

5 - 5 = ___

3 - 0 = ___

5 - 3 = ___

Finish

Have the student write the answers on the race track.

© ORIGO Education

a.

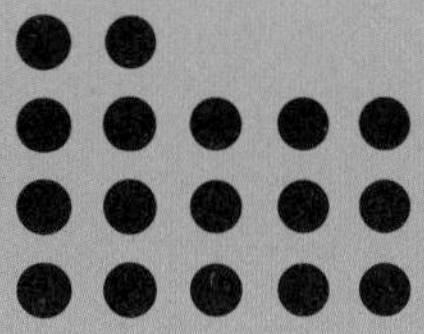

17

17

17

17

b.

18

18

18

18

c.

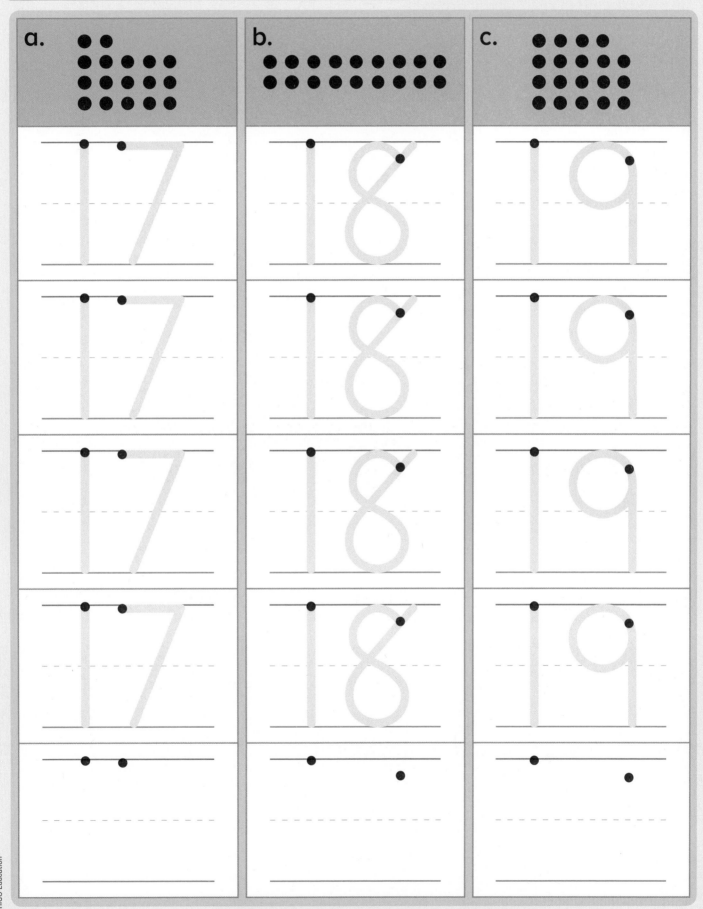

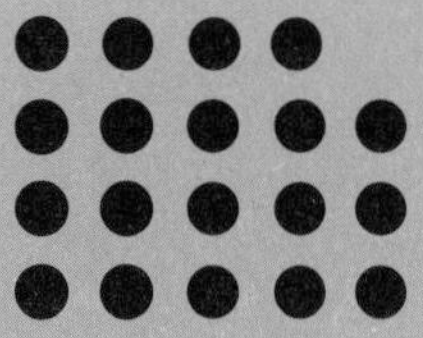

19

19

19

19

For each strip, ask the student to count the dots and say the matching number aloud. Then have the student write the numeral to match the number of dots.

© ORIGO Education

1	2	3	4	5	6	7	8	9	10	11	12	13	14	15	16	17	18	19	20

a.

one less		one greater
____	7	____

b.

one less		one greater
____	10	____

c.

one less		one greater
____	13	____

d.

one less		one greater
____	17	____

e.

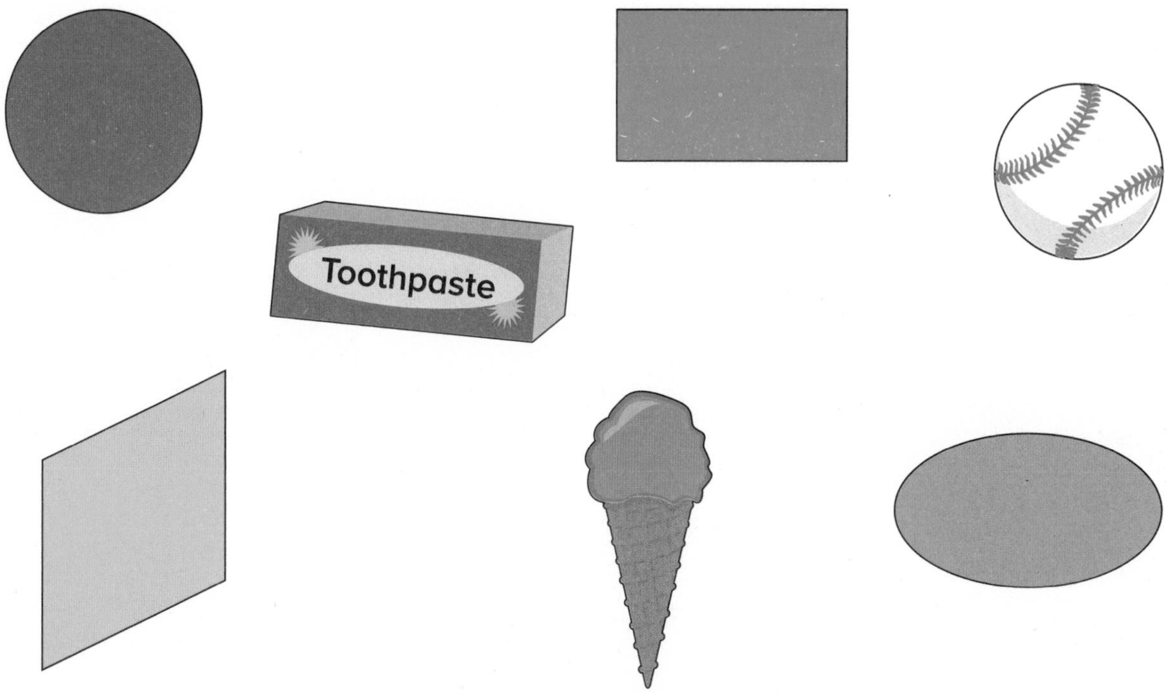

© ORIGO Education

Have the student write the numbers that are one less and one greater.
Then have the student circle the pictures of 3D objects.

one fewer		one more
	a. 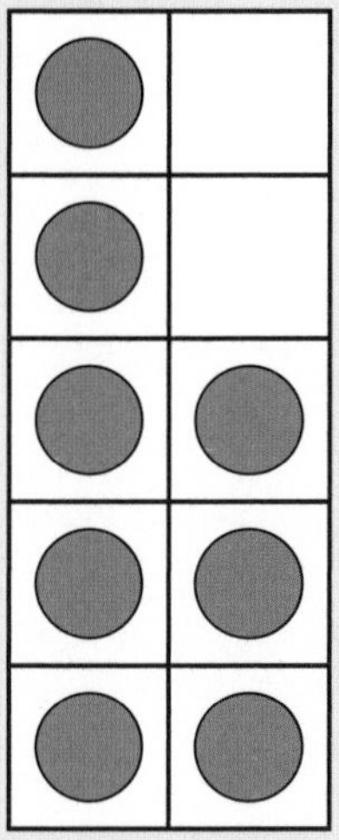	
	b. 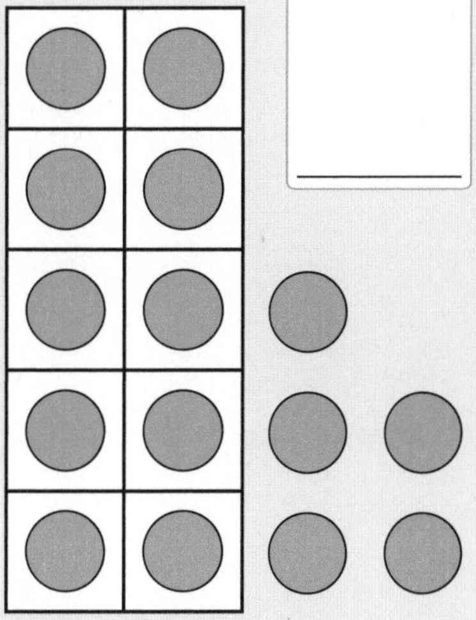	
	c. 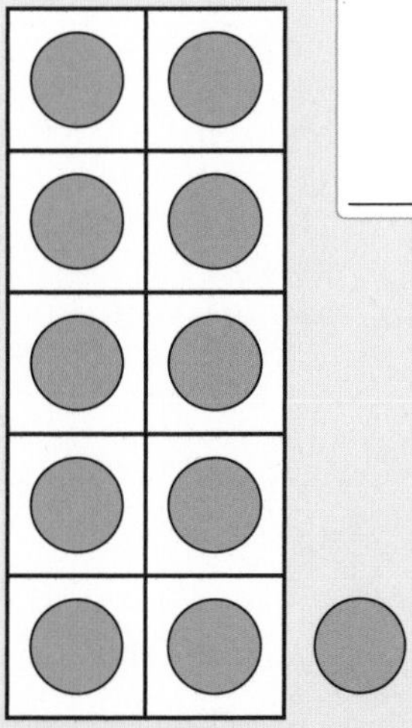	

© ORIGO Education

Have the student write the numeral to show the number of dots in each picture. Then have the student draw ◯ to show **one more** and then to show **one fewer**.

1	2	3	4	5	6	7	8	9	10	11	12	13	14	15	16	17	18	19	20

a.

one less		one greater
____	8	____

b.

one less		one greater
____	14	____

c.

one less		one greater
____	11	____

d.

one less		one greater
____	4	____

e.

one less		one greater
____	7	____

f.

one less		one greater
____	17	____

g.

one less		one greater
____	13	____

h.

one less		one greater
____	10	____

© ORIGO Education

Have the student write the numerals to represent the numbers that are **one less** and **one greater**.

a.  1 + 1 = ____

 1 + 0 = ____

b.  0 + 1 = ____

 2 + 0 = ____

c.  3 + 1 = ____

 2 + 2 = ____

d.  1 + 2 = ____

 1 + 4 = ____

e.  2 + 3 = ____

 3 + 0 = ____

© ORIGO Education

Have the student write all the totals, then draw a line from each bunch of flowers to a house with a matching total.

1	2	3	4	5	6	7	8	9	10	11	12	13	14	15	16	17	18	19	20

My number is

a. one greater than 15

b. one less than 4

c. between 8 and 10

d. one greater than 11

e. between 17 and 20

f. less than 7

g. greater than 13

h. between 4 and 12

© ORIGO Education

Ask the student to read each clue then write a number to match. Explain that some clues have more than one match.

1	2	3	4	5	6	7	8	9	10	11	12	13	14	15	16	17	18	19	20

My number

a. has 1 ten and 5 ones

b. has 2 tens and 0 ones

c. is 3 greater than 9

d. is 2 less than 17

e. add 3 makes 7

f. add 8 makes 10

g. subtract 2 is 6

h. subtract 5 is 1

© ORIGO Education

Have the student read each clue then write the matching number. They can use the number track to help their thinking.

a. $\square = 0 + 2$

4

b. $1 + 1 = \square$

c. $\square = 2 + 2$

2

d. $3 + 1 = \square$

e. $\square = 0 + 1$

1

f. $2 + 3 = \square$

g. $\square = 4 + 1$

5

h. $3 + 0 = \square$

i. $\square = 2 + 1$

3

j. $1 + 0 = \square$

© ORIGO Education

Have the student figure out and write the totals, then draw a line from each key to a matching door. There are two keys for each door.

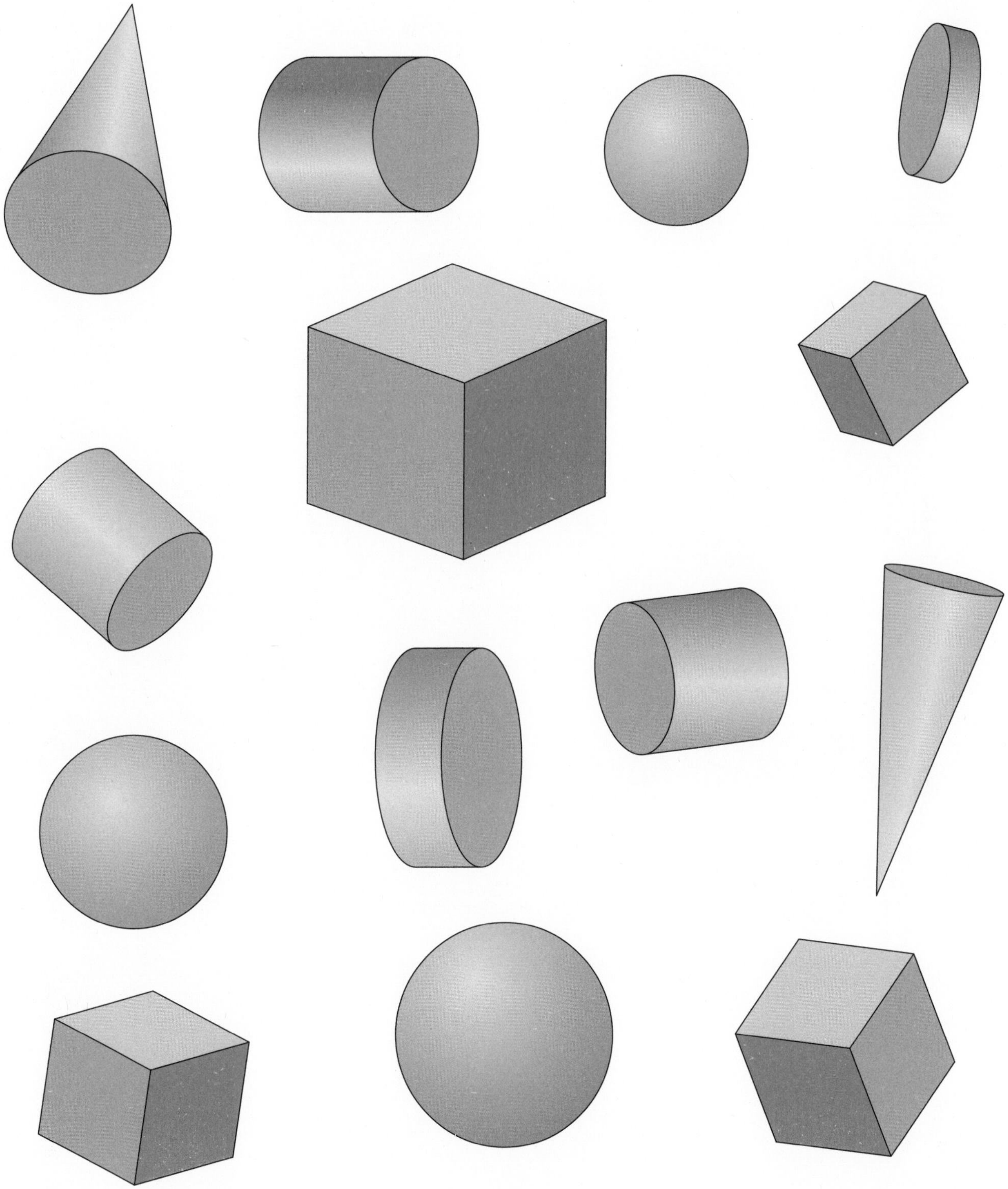

_____ spheres _____ cones _____ cylinders _____ cubes

© ORIGO Education

Have the student cross out all the pictures of spheres then write the total in the box. Ask the student to use a different color and repeat for each of the other objects.

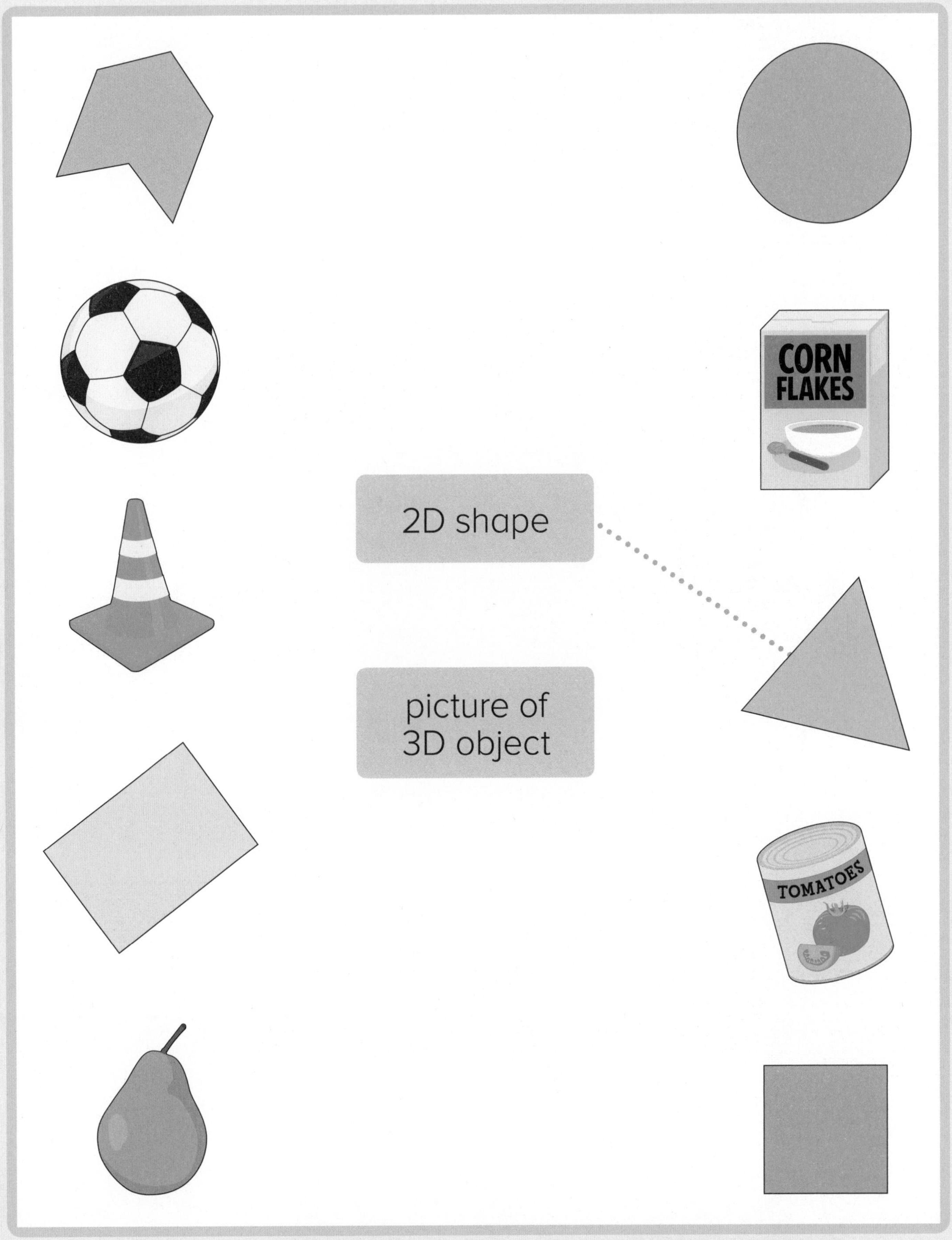

© ORIGO Education

Have the student look at each picture and decide if it is a 2D shape or a picture of a 3D object, then draw a line to the label to show their decision. Encourage the student to justify their decision.

a. 1 + 1 = ____

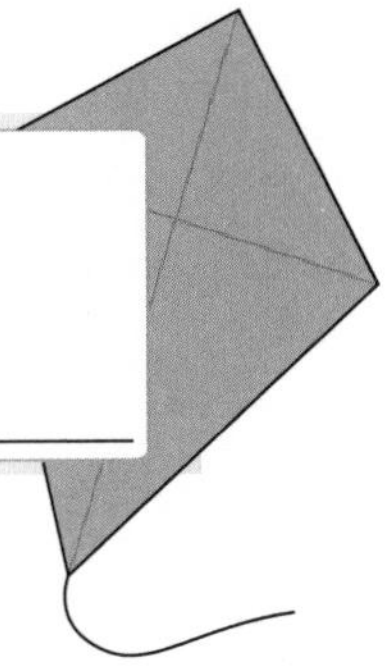

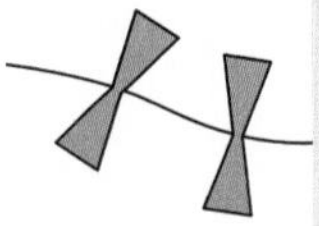

5 - 0 = ____

b. 2 + 3 = ____

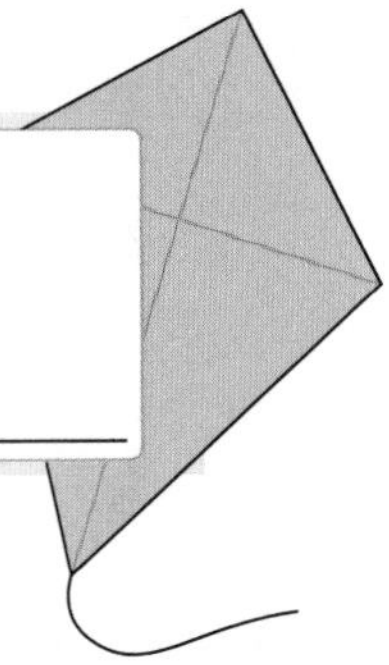

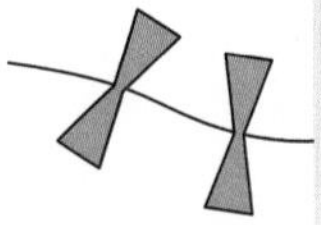

5 - 3 = ____

c. 2 + 2 = ____

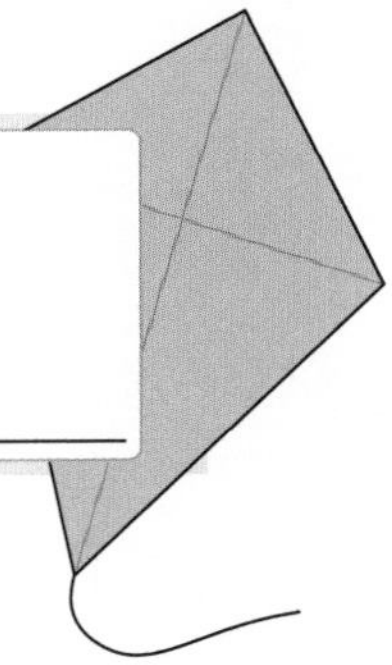

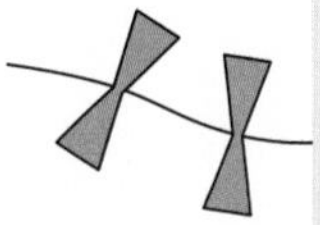

5 - 1 = ____

d. 2 + 1 = ____

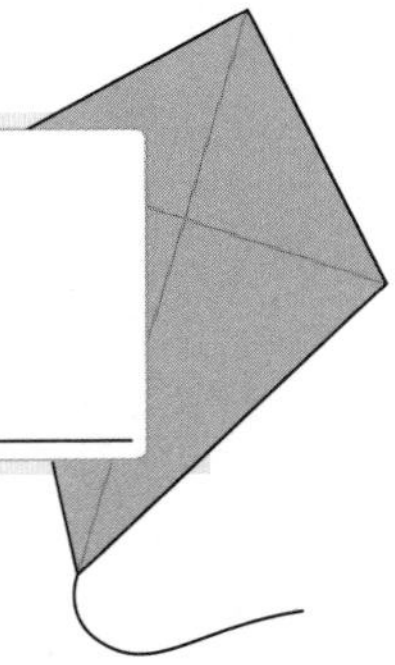

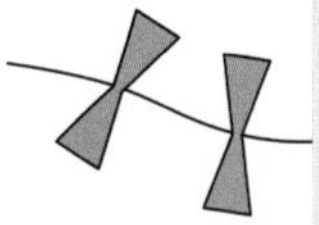

4 - 3 = ____

e. 0 + 1 = ____

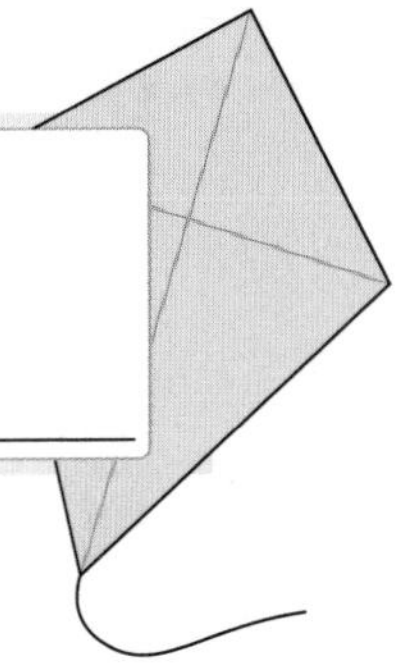

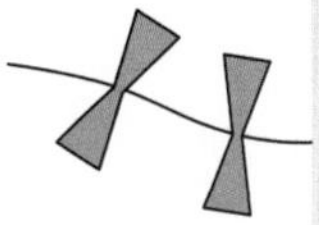

5 - 2 = ____

© ORIGO Education

Have the student figure out and write the answer on each kite and tail, then draw lines to join kites and tails that have the same answer.

a. ___ + 5 = ___

5 + ___ = ___

b. ___ + ___ = ___

___ + ___ = ___

c. ___ + ___ = ___

___ + ___ = ___

d. ___ + ___ = ___

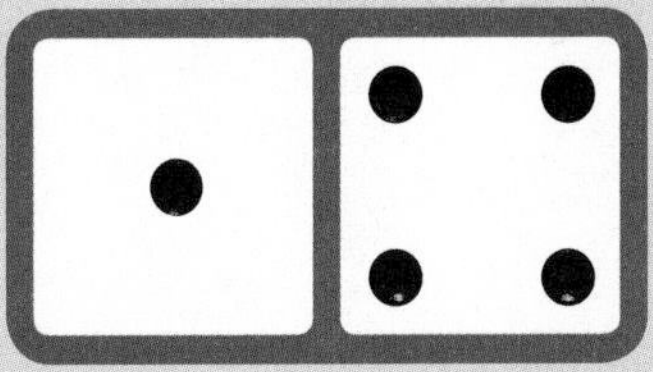

___ + ___ = ___

e.

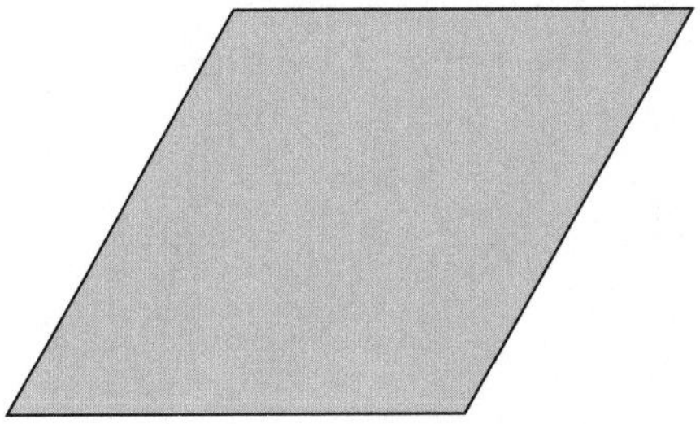

___ sides ___ corners

f.

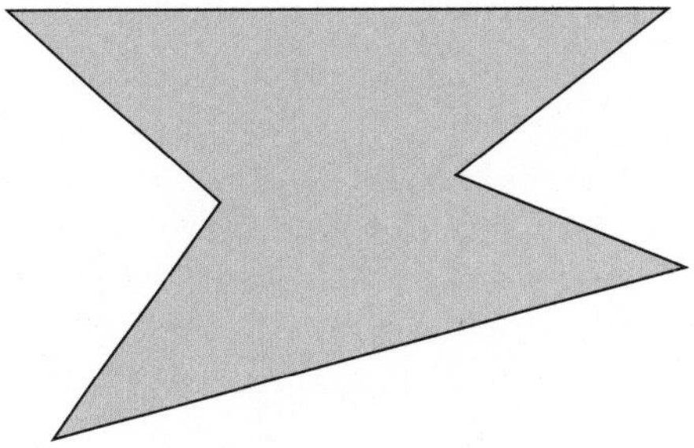

___ sides ___ corners

© ORIGO Education

Have the student write two equations to match each domino.
Then have the student write the number of sides and corners for each shape.

a.

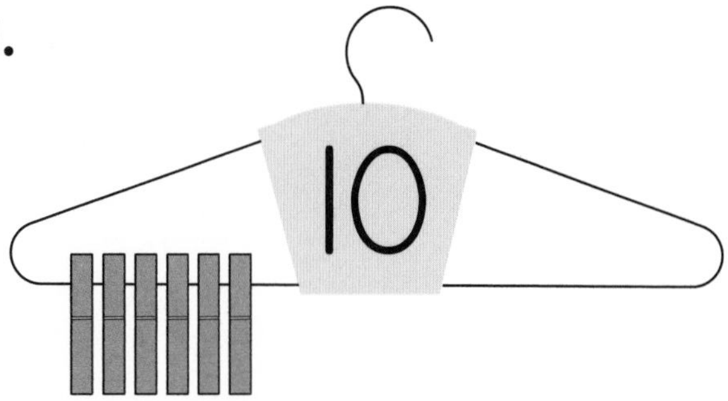

6 + ____ = ____

b.

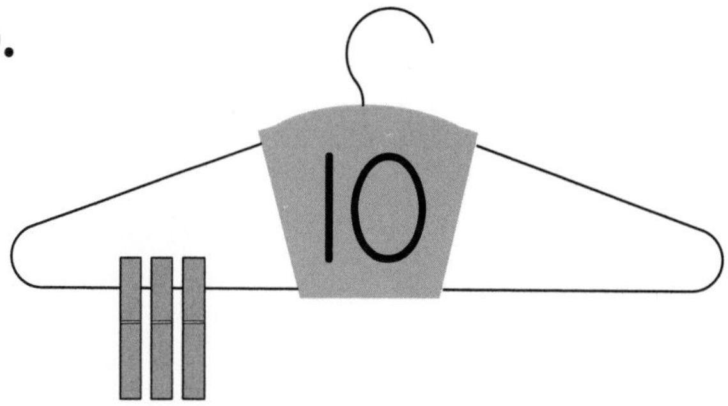

____ + ____ = ____

c.

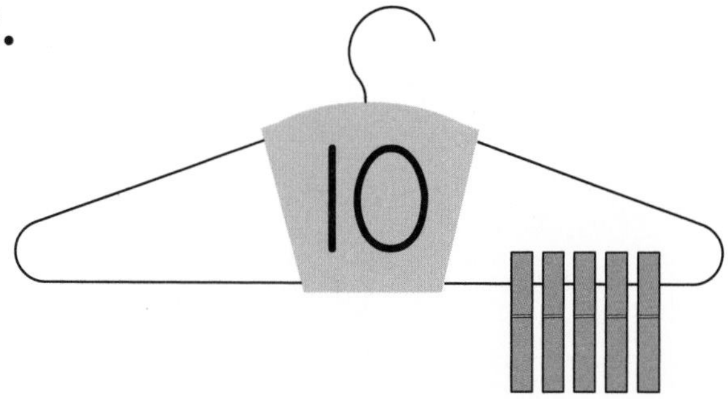

____ + ____ = ____

d.

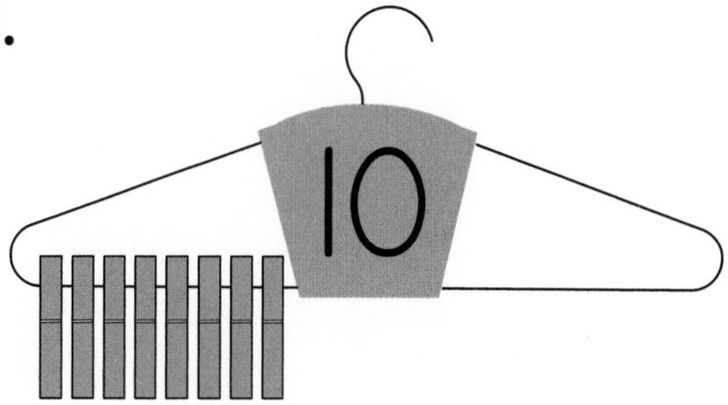

____ + ____ = ____

e.

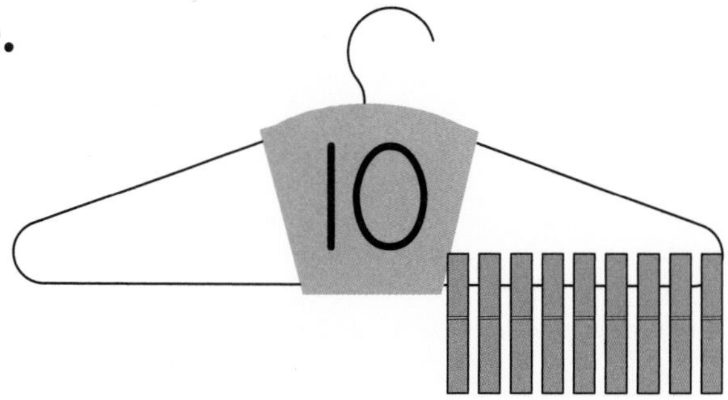

____ + ____ = ____

f.

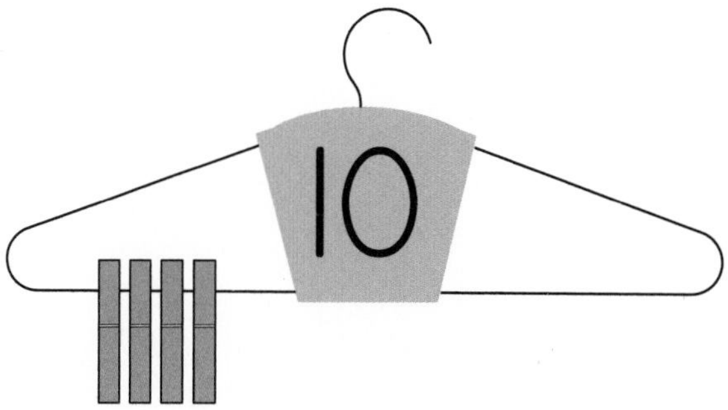

____ + ____ = ____

Have the student draw more clothespins to make a total of 10, then write the matching equation.

© ORIGO Education

a.

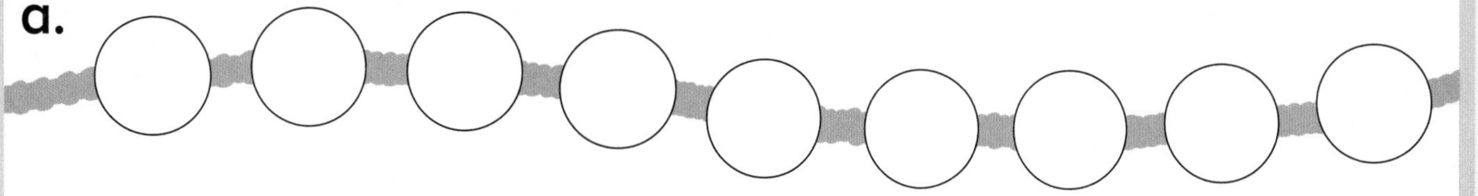

☐ + ☐ = ☐

b.

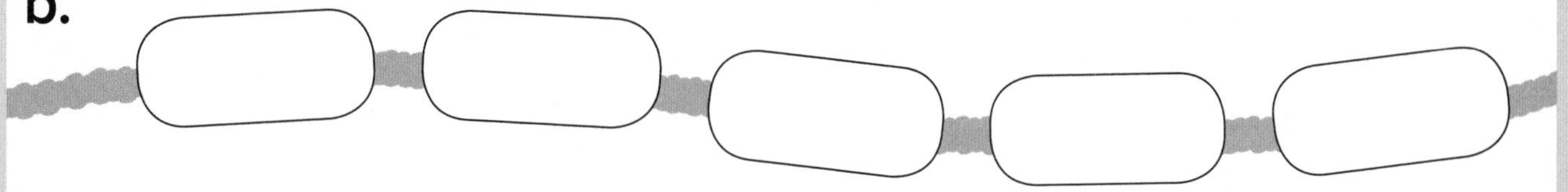

☐ + ☐ = ☐

c.

☐ + ☐ = ☐

d.

☐ + ☐ = ☐

For each string, ask the student to color some of the beads, then write an equation to match.

© ORIGO Education

Start	4 - 2 =	1 + 3 =	2 + 1 =	
	5 - 1 =	3 + 2 =	4 - 1 =	
	2 + 3 =	1 + 2 =	5 - 3 =	
	2 + 2 =	1 + 4 =	3 + 1 =	
	0 + 5 =	4 - 3 =	1 + 3 =	
	1 + 1 =	5 - 4 =	2 + 0 =	
	5 - 5 =	4 + 1 =	5 - 2 =	Finish

© ORIGO Education

Have the student figure out each answer and write it on the track.

a.

1 + 6 = ___

6 + 1 = ___

b.

___ + ___ = ___

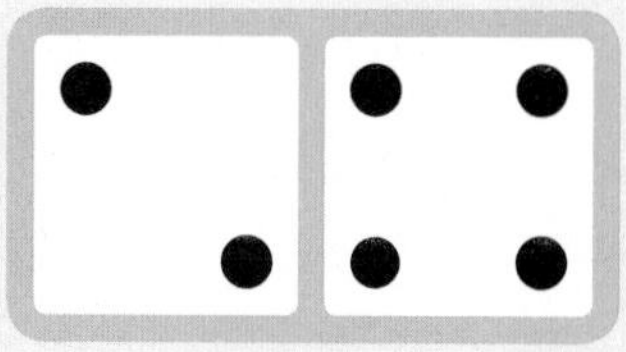

___ + ___ = ___

c.

___ + ___ = ___

___ + ___ = ___

d.

___ + ___ = ___

___ + ___ = ___

e.

___ + ___ = ___

___ + ___ = ___

f.

___ + ___ = ___

___ + ___ = ___

© ORIGO Education

Have the student write two equations to match each domino.

a.

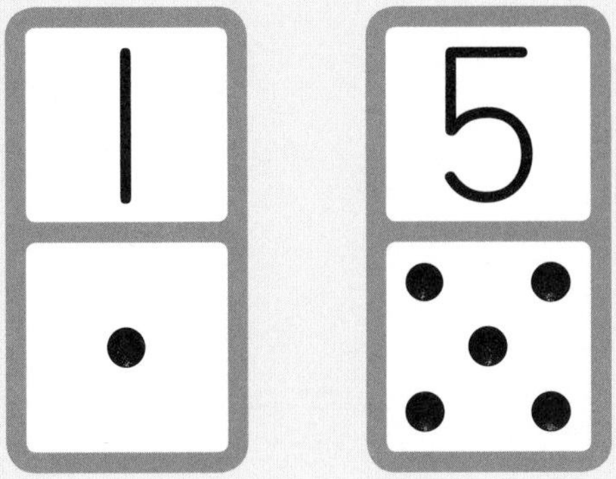

____ + ____ = ____

b.

____ + ____ = ____

c.

____ + ____ = ____

d.

____ + ____ = ____

e.

____ + ____ = ____

f.

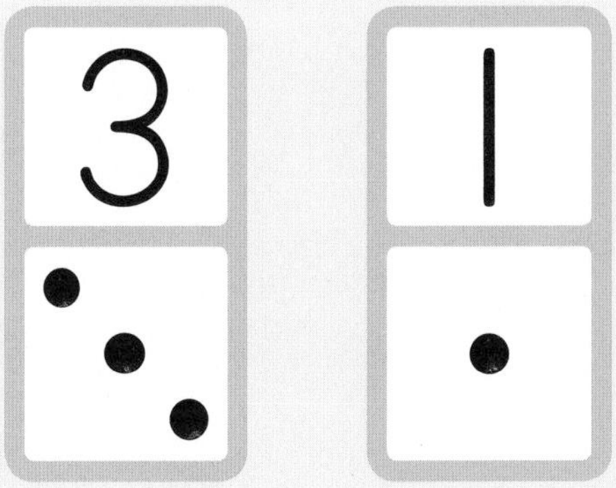

____ + ____ = ____

Have the student say the greater number, then count on to figure out the total. Then ask the student to write the equation with the greater number first.

© ORIGO Education

a. 3 + 2 =

b. 1 + 4 =

c. 1 + 2 =

d. 2 + 2 = 4

e. 3 + 1 =

1   2   3   4   5

f. 4 − 3 =

g. 4 − 2 =

h. 5 − 2 =

i. 3 − 1 =

j. 5 − 4 =

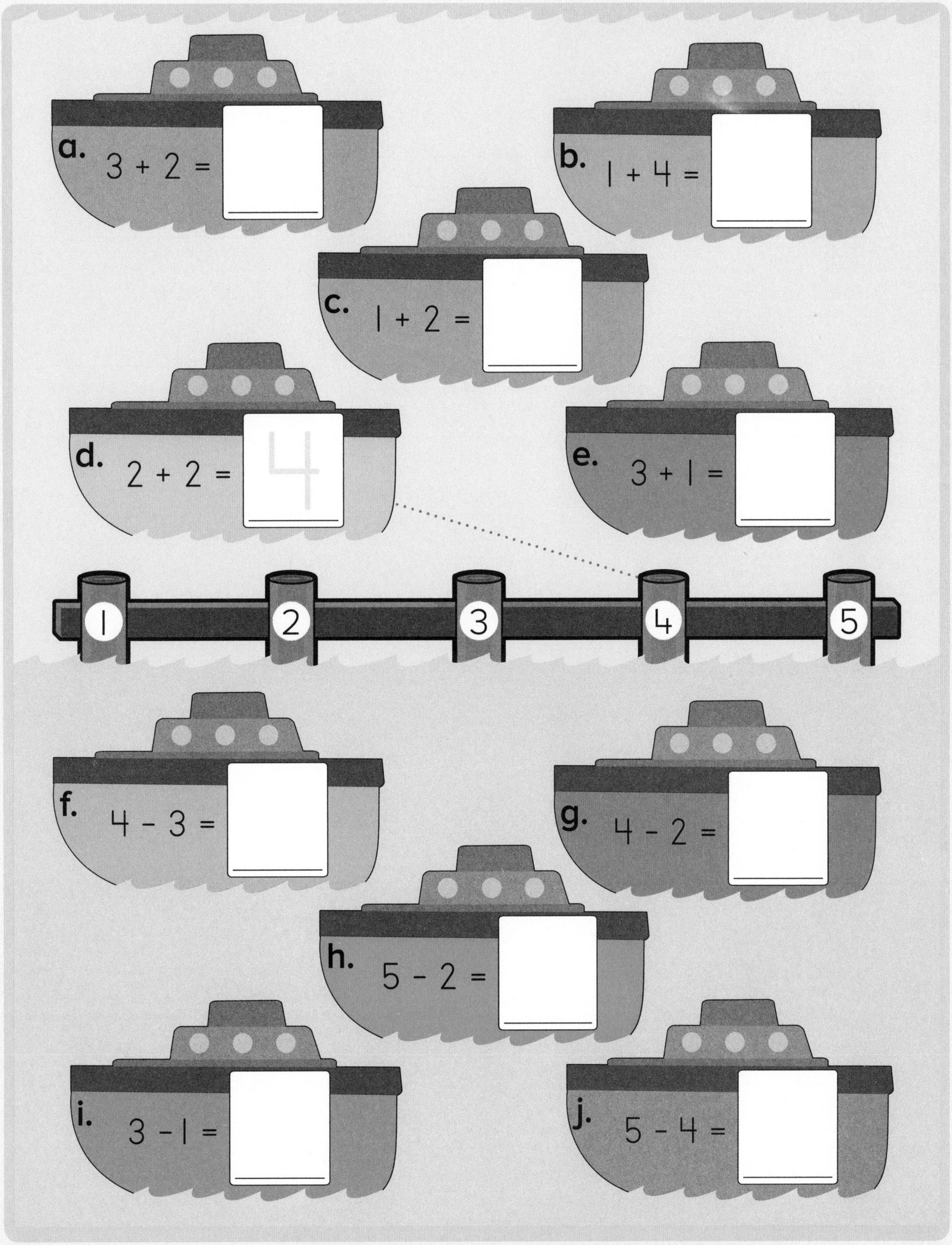

Have the student write the answer on each boat, then draw a line to a matching answer on the pier.

© ORIGO Education

a. circles	b. triangles
c. squares	**d. non-square rectangles**

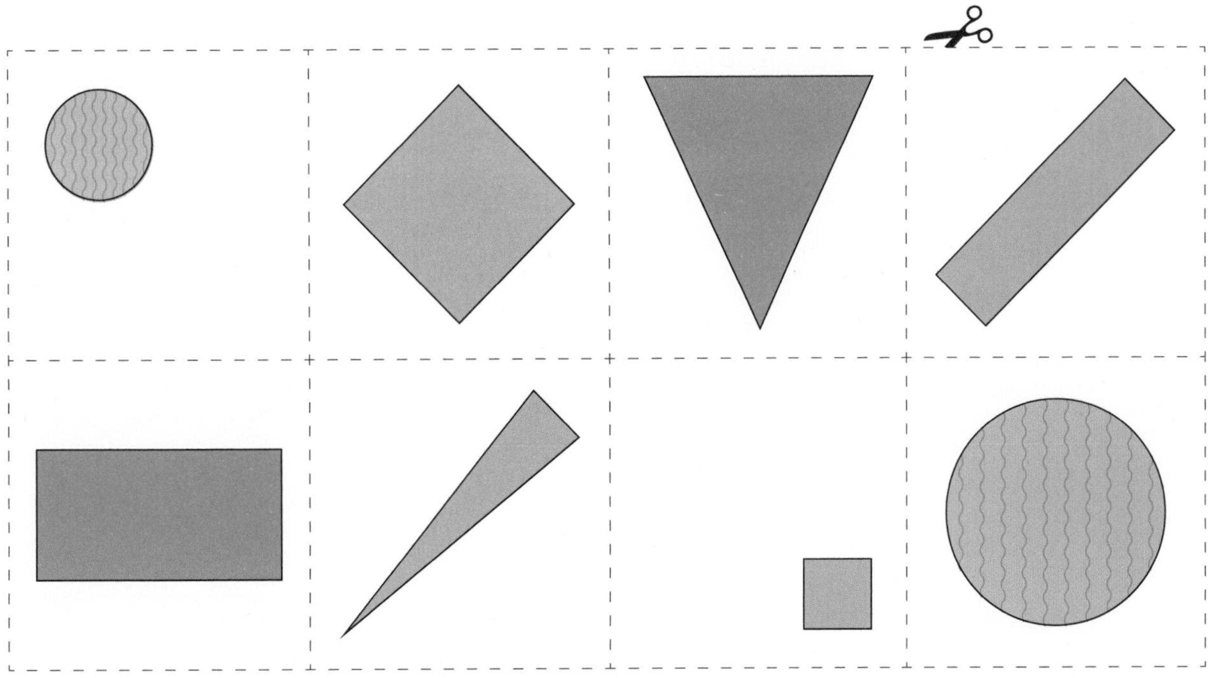

© ORIGO Education

Have the student cut out the 2D shapes, then sort and paste them in the correct box.

a.

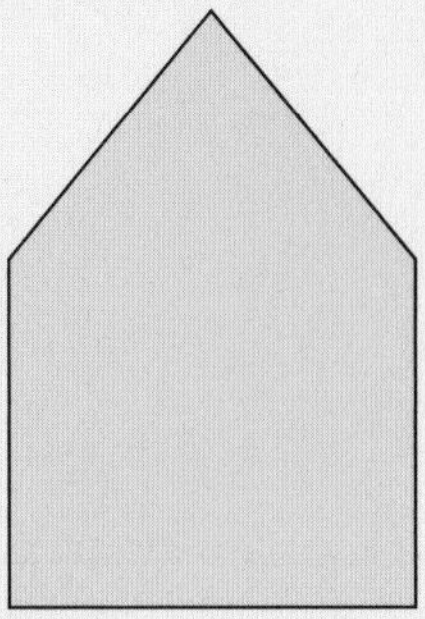

_____ sides _____ corners

b.

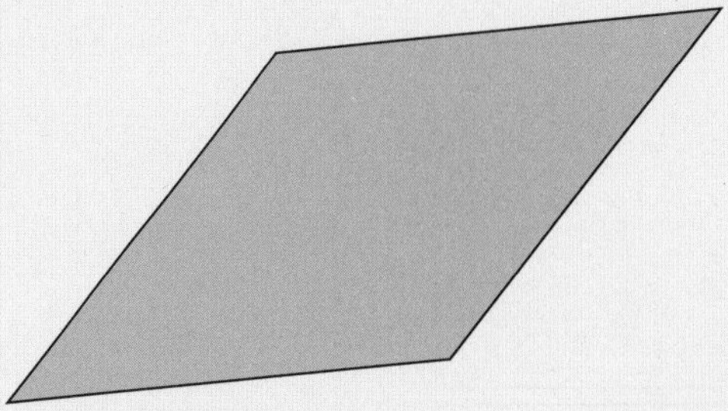

_____ sides _____ corners

c.

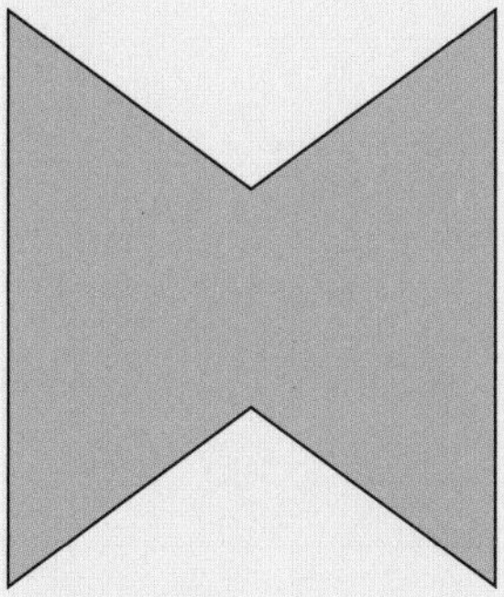

_____ sides _____ corners

d.

_____ sides _____ corners

e.

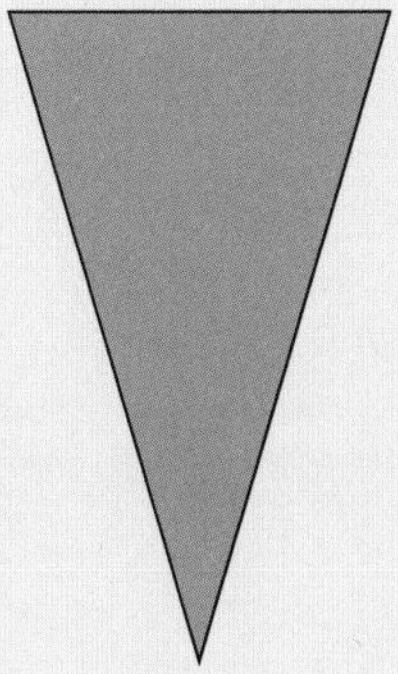

_____ sides _____ corners

f.

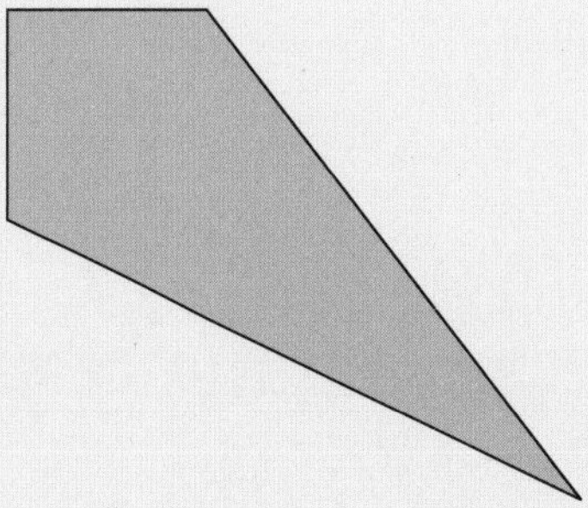

_____ sides _____ corners

© ORIGO Education

Have the student count and write the number of sides and corners for each shape.

a. 2 + 2 = ____

b. 1 + 4 = ____

c. 4 - 3 = ____

d. 5 - 2 = ____

e. 3 - 3 = ____

f. 1 + 1 = ____

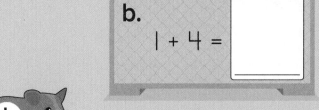

© ORIGO Education

Have the student write the answer on each cage, then draw a line to the matching hamster.

a. Dallas sees 4 small crabs on the beach. 3 of the crabs hide. How many crabs can still be seen?

b. Ashley uses 6 blue buttons and 3 red buttons to make a pattern. How many buttons did she use?

c. The blue team has 4 people and the red team has 4 people. How many people are there in total?

d. Gabriel has 7 strawberries. He eats 2 of them. How many strawberries are left?

e.

© ORIGO Education

Have the student use small objects to act out each problem and write an equation to show the answer. Then ask the student to copy the picture.

a. There are 6 eggs in the nest. 3 eggs hatch. How many eggs have not hatched?	+	–
b. Mom bought some bananas and used 4 in a cake. There are 2 bananas left over. How many bananas did Mom buy?	+	–
c. Camila has 8 dollars. Her uncle gives her 1 dollar more. How many dollars does she have now?	+	–
d. There were 9 roses on the bush. Dad picked 2 roses. How many roses are still on the bush?	+	–
e. There are 5 eggs in one nest and 2 eggs in another nest. How many eggs are there in total?	+	–
f. 8 children are playing in the park. Then 4 children go home. How many children are still at the park?	+	–
g. There were 7 frogs on the riverbank. 3 frogs jump into the water. How many frogs are still on the riverbank?	+	–

Have the student circle + or – to show how to solve each problem.

© ORIGO Education

a. There are 4 brown chickens and 3 red chickens. How many chickens are there in total?

b. Mom baked 10 muffins. She ate 2 muffins. How many muffins are left?

c. 9 friends are playing in the pool. 4 friends get out. How many friends are now in the pool?

d. There are 5 boys and one girl in the playground. How many children are in the playground?

e. Tama had 3 pennies. He found 2 more pennies. How many pennies does he have now?

f. There were 8 eggs in the carton. Dad used 3 eggs for breakfast. How many eggs are left?

© ORIGO Education

For each of these, have the student use small objects to act out the problem, then write an equation to show the answer.

Start	4 - 2 =	3 - 1 =	3 + 2 =	
	4 + 1 =	0 + 5 =	2 + 1 =	
	2 + 2 =	1 + 3 =	5 - 1 =	
	2 + 0 =	5 - 3 =	4 - 3 =	
	1 + 4 =	1 + 1 =	2 + 3 =	
	4 - 1 =	5 - 0 =	2 - 2 =	
	3 + 1 =	5 - 4 =	4 - 0 =	Finish

© ORIGO Education

Have the student figure out each answer and write it on the track.

a. There are 7 balloons. 3 balloons fly away.
How many balloons are left?

b. There are 3 yellow parrots and 2 green parrots.
How many parrots are there in total?

c. Aston has 9 books to read. He reads 3 books on Saturday. How many books does he have left to read?

d. There are 6 girls and 2 boys on the team.
How many children are on the team?

© ORIGO Education

Ask the student to draw a picture to solve each problem. Then have them write an equation to show the answer.

a. Grace read 3 books in one week and then 5 more books the next week. How many books did Grace read in the two weeks?

b. There were 9 sheep on a farm. 4 sheep were sold. How many sheep are left?

c. There are 10 flowers in a vase. 3 flowers are red and the rest are yellow. How many yellow flowers are in the vase?

d. Dad made 4 grilled cheese sandwiches and 4 peanut butter sandwiches. How many sandwiches did he make in total?

e. Mom and Dad blew up 10 balloons at the party. Mom blew up 5 of the balloons. How many did Dad blow up?

f. There are 3 goats and 6 cows on a farm. How many animals are there in total?

© ORIGO Education

Ask the student to write an equation to solve each problem.

a. 3 + 2 = ☐

b. 3 - 2 = ☐

c. 2 + 1 = ☐

d. 4 - 1 = ☐

e. 1 + 0 = ☐

f. 5 - 0 = ☐

g. 5 - 1 = ☐

h. 5 - 3 = ☐

i. 2 + 2 = ☐

j. 2 + 0 = ☐

© ORIGO Education

Have the student write all the answers. Then have the student color nets and butterflies with matching answers, using a different color for each pair.

a.

b.

c.

© ORIGO Education

Have the student copy each picture. Then ask the student to say all the shape names they know.

paste

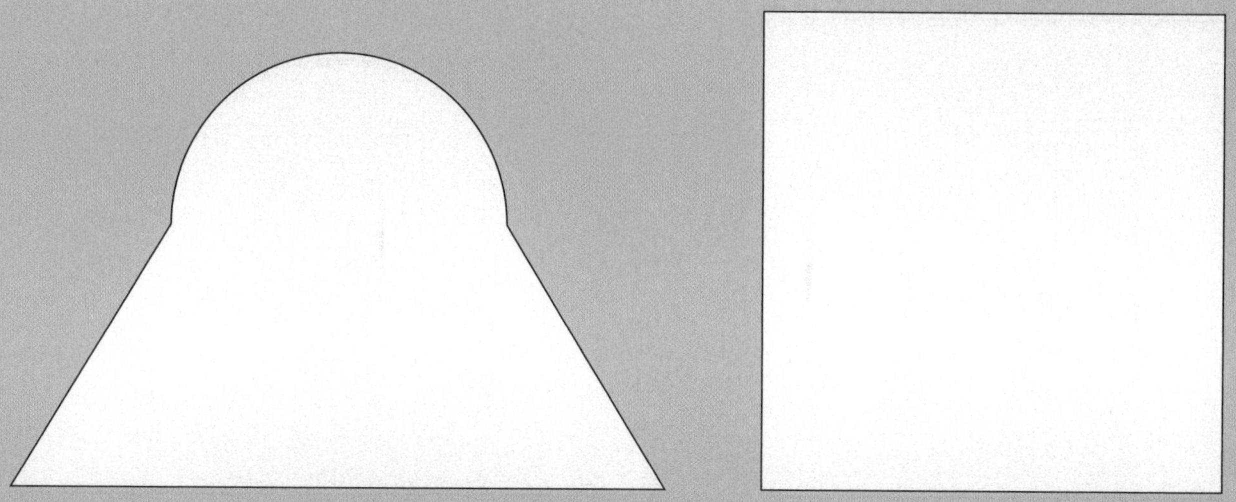

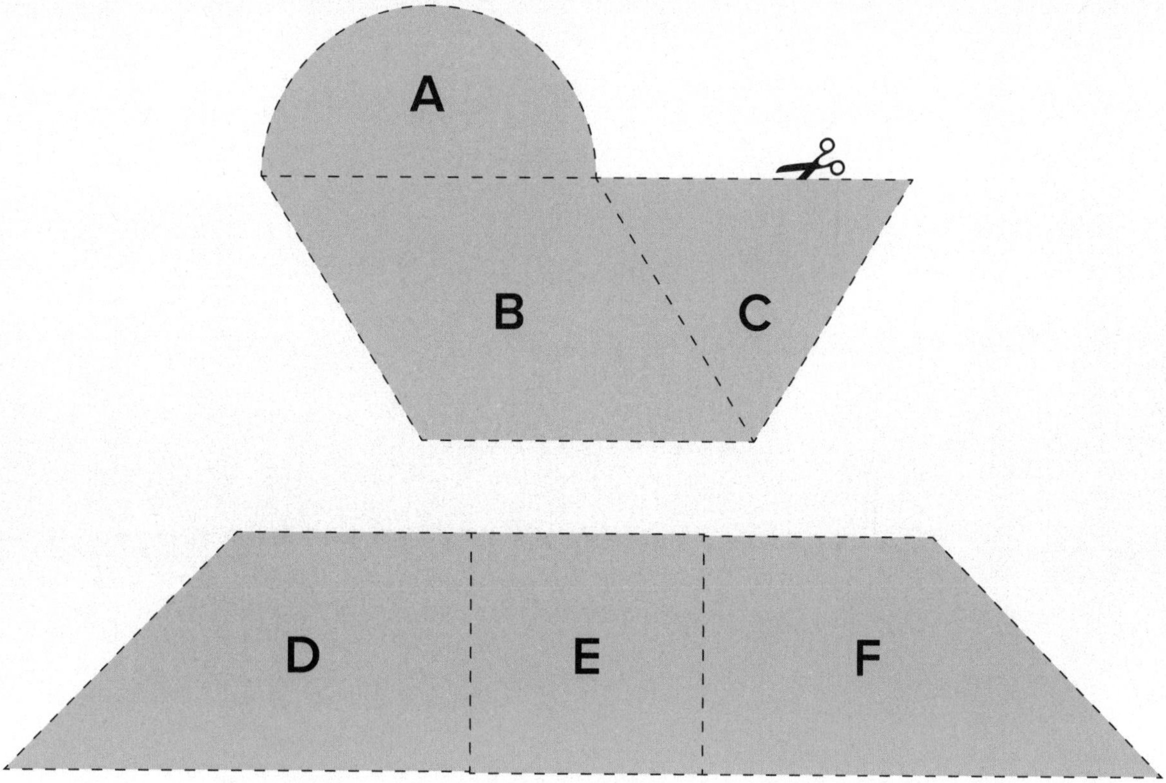

© ORIGO Education

Have the student cut along all the dotted lines to make six shapes, then paste the shapes above to match each outline.

Start	5 - 4 = ____	0 + 1 = ____	2 + 2 = ____	
	1 + 1 = ____	1 + 3 = ____	2 - 1 = ____	
	3 + 2 = ____	1 - 1 = ____	4 + 1 = ____	
	3 - 2 = ____	0 + 2 = ____	2 + 3 = ____	
	1 + 4 = ____	4 - 3 = ____	5 - 5 = ____	
	5 + 0 = ____	3 + 1 = ____	2 + 1 = ____	
	4 - 2 = ____	5 - 3 = ____	4 + 0 = ____	Finish

© ORIGO Education

Have the student figure out each answer and write it on the track.

a.

17 cents

b.

12 cents

c.

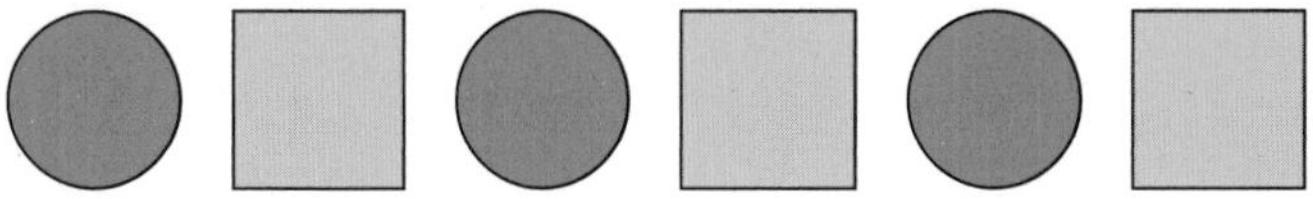

d.

© ORIGO Education

Ask the student to cut out coins from page 235 and paste them to show the amount on each price tag in two different ways. Then ask the student to draw more shapes to continue the patterns.

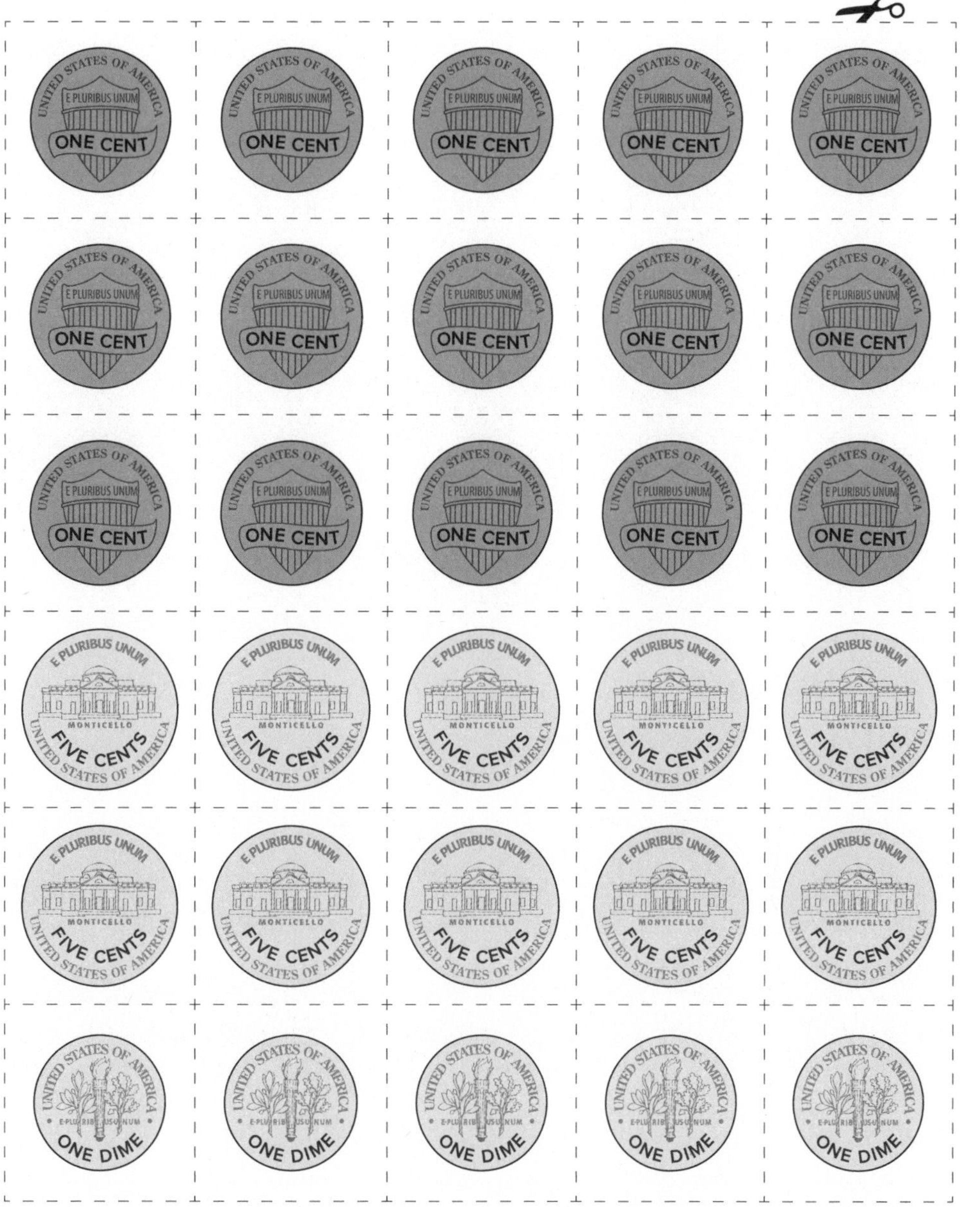

© ORIGO Education